Suns Go Down

THE MACMILLAN COMPANY
NEW YORK · BOSTON · CHICAGO · DALLAS
ATLANTA · SAN FRANCISCO

MACMILLAN & CO., Limited
LONDON · BOMBAY · CALCUTTA
MELBOURNE

THE MACMILLAN COMPANY
OF CANADA, Limited
TORONTO

SUNS
GO
DOWN

BY

FLANNERY LEWIS

NEW YORK
THE MACMILLAN COMPANY
1937

PRINTED IN THE UNITED STATES OF AMERICA
BY THE STRATFORD PRESS, INC., NEW YORK

Presentiment is that long shadow on the lawn
Indicative that suns go down;
The notice to the startled grass
That darkness is about to pass.
                    —EMILY DICKINSON.

Because I know that clocks must tick
    Our lives to dust someday,
I will wind up the music box
    And listen to it play.
                    —RACHEL FIELD.

ERRATA

Franklin Leonard, representing the Comstock Tunnel & Drainage Company with offices at 48 South B Street, Virginia City, Nevada, and Alan Bible, District Attorney of Storey County, Nevada, have pointed out numerous misstatements of fact made by author Lewis and printed in the book "Suns Go Down," particularly relating to the mining and milling operations now being conducted successfully on the Comstock Lode, at Virginia City, Nevada.

These men report that during the calendar year 1936 the Comstock Lode produced in excess of $1,000,000. in gold and silver bullion; that the roads leading to the Comstock and passing through Virginia City are not trails but are perfectly graded, hard-surfaced automobile roads constructed during the past year at a cost of more than $500,000.; that automobile traffic is so heavy and Virginia City is now so active that traffic regulations, including STOP signs at cross streets are now in use; that Virginia City now has all important facilities for successful mine operations and development, namely, deep drainage, ample water supply, electric power and transportation; that the community has plenty of stores, restaurants and garages conducted by substantial business men and women; a telephone central office; eight reduction plants shipping bullion, or concentrates; all houses occupied and many new ones recently erected; that there is a new $35,000. school house; that there are both high school and grade schools, and churches; and in fact that Virginia City today is in all respects a thriving, law-abiding community.

This erratum slip is placed in the book by the publishers so that the author's story will not be taken as factual representation of Virginia City today.

The Beginning

The Beginning

I REMEMBER THAT IN THE WINTER
MONTHS, IN THE SNOW SEASON, IT GOT
dark very early in Virginia City, in Nevada. The
lamps had to be lighted for supper in those days; and
after supper, when the dishes were done and the woodbox was filled, there was very little for a young boy
and his grandmother to do. Sometimes we listened to
the graphophone that had cylindrical records, but
mostly Grandmother read to me. She usually read
stories of families in towns in New England, and I
now remember that I disliked the stories, for New
England did seem a dull place. But Grandmother has
always been a New England person, even to calling
her apron a pinafore; although she has been more than
seventy years in Nevada, she still speaks of the West
as the Bad Lands.

Grandmother had come to the West when she was
barely sixteen and a bride, in the time that gold was
discovered and Virginia City had until then only men
and prostitutes and Piute women. It is difficult to imagine my grandmother as she was then, a very young

woman. So far as I can recall, she has always been the same, a small and slight person with gray hair and a light Irish complexion that seemed determined when she was fifty years old never to admit another day of age. Even Grandmother's clothing kept a style that stopped for sure at the turn of the century.

But in years Grandmother is very old now, so old, indeed, she has forgotten she is ninety. It is an accomplishment to become that old in the West; but it is not likely that Grandmother would be proud if she knew precisely how many years she has lived, for she thinks that old people are a problem, and she, for one, will have nothing to do with them.

When Grandmother read to me of New England and I protested, she would shrug and explain she was reading about civilization and people who had standards and stuck to them, and that I would do well to listen. She seemed so fond of New England that I wondered as I grew older why she had never returned there. She had the chance, and it did seem her thoughts returned there in the evening. But it is too late now, of course.

Her home has been her home for seventy-three years, and she knows it is the only home in the West that is fit to be lived in. She thinks architects are a misled lot these days. They can follow a vogue and be ornate enough, but not one of them knows how to build a good solid home to keep out the cold and stand firm through a blizzard. Grandmother has admitted these last few years that her home may be old-fashioned. She will concede that just to avoid argument. But she is never likely to know that her home is so old it is hopeless.

It is a large house with a parlor, a sitting room, a spacious kitchen, of course; four bedrooms, and a room or two that have been boarded up. It is easy to tell what Grandmother thinks of a visitor by the room into which he is led. Old friends come to the sitting room, where the sun is in the afternoon. It is a pleasant place with light pine furniture and a sewing machine and a sofa. The sitting room also has a canary, a very old bird but still a sullen one. The ladies who lived in Virginia City before the town was deserted met in the sitting room, where tea was served and other ladies were pleasantly disparaged.

The sitting room is the place for murmurs and occasional agitation, but the parlor has always demanded distinct and careful conversation, for the parlor is reserved for people of importance, such as the current Governor of Nevada or Mr. and Mrs. Dwight of the Reno & Carson City Transportation & Water Supply. When Grandmother's family was young, a member of it could scarcely ever get into the parlor unless he were in love or dead, and in either exception he had to be formal about it. The sunlight cannot get in, either, for it has always been regarded as a menace that could hurt the rugs and fade the furniture. The sitting room might casually join in and help with the visit, but the parlor must maintain its excessive hauteur, to remain aloof, cool and immaculate and, indeed, almost precious.

The parlor was until recently impressive and elegant with heavy mahogany furniture and cushions of rose plush, shipped from the East to San Francisco and carried by cart over the Sierra Nevadas to Virginia City. Grandmother had warned the teamsters that a mar on it meant trouble, but the furniture came swathed in sacking and without a scratch.

The parlor demanded that one be dressed to his best, to the hilt, with high collar and a suit that had been properly brushed. The chairs would have been offended at anything else, yet, even if one prepared for them, they seemed to resent being sat in.

There were also books in the parlor for lack of a library, but they were severe and solemn in well dressed editions of Shakespeare, Carlyle, and Dante, and were the books that nobody read. They had been dusted, though, every day for fifty years, just like the tiny but elaborate trinkets on the whatnot, which were gratifying miniatures but, for want of people important enough, were seldom seen. That parlor was indeed a snobbish place, and I imagine that even Grandmother has been uncomfortable in it.

It isn't likely that Mark Twain was ever in the parlor; Grandmother, at any rate, would never have invited him in. He was one of her husband's friends who could come to the kitchen. At that time she referred to him as the printer. He *was* the city editor of the *Enterprise*, but that didn't make a bit of difference to Grandmother, for he printed calling cards for ladies and gentlemen, menus for restaurants, and he had something to do with the newspaper that Wally brought to the house in the afternoon. Even when he, too, became a person of importance in the East and entitled to the parlor, Grandmother spoke of him as "that printer, Clemens, whatever became of him?"

The kitchen is easily the best room of all. It is large and plain and laid with a heavy board floor and woven Piute rugs. Heavy pine benches and a broad work table have been built into the wall, and because they are pine and have been polished with use, they seem very comfortable as they grow older. The table is covered with an oilcloth, a patent cloth of some kind that has a bright design. The cloth is changed each month, but Grandmother retains the design, which is invariably the Capitol and grounds at Sacramento, in California. Grandmother retains it because the grounds have lawns and maple trees, and Virginia City has neither. While the oilcloth is new, it is slippery and has a store odor.

In the winter time the kitchen is very cheerful, with its bright oilcloth and its Piute rugs and the pine benches freshly shellacked. It is always warm and dry from the range, and Grandmother's friends, who like her very well, would rather be there than in the parlor.

It has become difficult, though, for friends to visit Grandmother, now that Virginia City is deserted. The weather protests, and the roads are rough, and except for Grandmother, there isn't any other reason for returning to Virginia City. Unfortunately, though, the tourists come in the summer time, grinding their cars over the Geiger Grade, eager to see the remains of the Comstock Lode. Virginia City is so high in the mountains that tourists who don't realize the altitude are sometimes overcome. Grandmother refuses to accept this as a fact. She dislikes tourists, for they are bothersome, and even if they faint she suspects they are just trying to attract attention.

In this high place there is always a wind, and it is usually a whining wind that seemed, when I was very young, to be trying to come into the house. Grandmother insisted my fears were nonsense. She would point out that the wind was a busy man and had too many other places to go; yet even she only half believed it, for when she looked through the kitchen window into the dark where the trees were bending, she drew her shawl closer about her shoulders and invariably put more wood in the range.

My grandmother told stories about the wind. He was the Washoe Zephyr who came up from Washoe Lake, and he was the villain of the seasons. He never got anybody but he tore blooms from the trees and whispered to families of their mortgages. He came every day to stamp and blow his breath as hard as he could, but he never got into the house and in his frustration he inevitably became indignant. He was like the villains in the melodrama, she said; he could threaten with furious impatience, yet in the end he had to coax with a whine.

The wood was kept high in the range while Grandmother frustrated the Washoe Zephyr. That range roared all winter long. It was capable of such rage it could tremble with heat, and it was large enough to defy a blizzard, as indeed it did many times. On a cold night it was very pleasant to sit by the range. The pleasure was always interrupted, though, by the problem of going to bed. When it was time to go to bed, Grandmother and I had a game we would play. It was called "Going Out to See How the Pigeons Are and Then Going to Bed." Grandmother insisted it was bad luck for the pigeons if only one of us went out to see them. They would feel neglected. Besides, there

- 9 -

were two of them, and just one of us could not properly look after both of them. Grandmother and I always went out together, and the pigeons were always all right.

Our bedrooms were side by side in the wing of the house, and we would go together to them, too. Walking through the dark of the hallway, Grandmother would hold my hand; so I wouldn't stumble, she explained. Sometimes on these trips she would sing. Grandmother does not sing very well, but those nights she could sing loudly; loudly at least for a house that lay so quiet with the snow around it that you felt you should whisper.

I told the grocer's deliveryman about our game, but Grandmother laughed with fervor and explained to him that it was the only way she could get me to bed at a decent hour. This was one of the few times that Grandmother bothered to explain herself; the game continued, but it was never again discussed.

For that matter, there are many subjects that Grandmother has never discussed. She seldom speaks of Virginia City. It doesn't seem to interest her much, although from time to time she has been hailed by Fourth of July orators as "the first decent white woman in the Comstock District," which seems to be an extraordinary honor, although Grandmother regards it with dismay. Orators seemed determined to persuade her that she is really a fine, old relic; to make her feel, she said, as old as an institution.

"If this talk continues," she said, "I am likely to become a landmark. People will be directing tourists to drive up Gold Hill to the Divide and turn east at Nellie Flannery."

Grandmother, though, did see the town from its beginning. In her youth that high land, so dry and harsh, had been with its gold the making of San Francisco. The gold brought Nevada into the Union and paid a great deal of the Civil War debt. For a generation it was wealthy, and the homes it had were magnificent in what Grandmother considered deplorable taste. She has been forever conscious of the land of gold; there were reminders of it in so casual a task as paying a call to a neighbor, for the carriage that came for her would have handles of gold surely, and the proud horses would often be shod with it.

Such days as these were a long time ago, and Virginia City has changed almost entirely since then. Indeed, its change would be complete if it were not for Grandmother, for now its mines are closed and its gold is gone, and in the last fifty years it has lost the forty thousand families who once lived there.

From her home on the Divide, Grandmother can see the abandoned blocks of old houses down in the town, which is in itself part of the mountain. There is seldom traffic down there, and the roadways are indistinct, and the buildings are slowly settling into the undermined earth.

When a horse and carriage or an automobile comes over the Grade now, the dogs run out and bark at it in bewilderment. The few men who stay in the town to salvage and mill the discarded gold ore are not the pioneers or even the remnants of them, but stragglers from the city who are weary with work and reasonably orderly in their conduct. Yet when Grandmother looks down from the height of the Divide, she sees a city that she still dislikes vaguely, for she thinks of its people as pioneers, and for Grandmother pioneers have always been rough and crude and entirely too noisy.

Perhaps in a few years the mountain will be rid of its town and Grandmother won't be bothered any more by pioneers. The cycle seems impatient to complete itself, but it would have to disturb Grandmother, and Grandmother would never stand for that.

Chapter Two

Chapter Two

GRANDMOTHER WOULD NOT LIKE TO BE TOLD SHE RAN AWAY FROM HOME TO be married. She would insist the marriage was in no sense an elopement, either. She had simply, as she said, gone away with her husband of the day before, on a ship for San Francisco, without letting anyone know she was leaving. It was that and nothing more, and it occurred one drowsy morning in April on a day that was otherwise uneventful; so drowsy and uneventful indeed that perhaps her passing would scarcely have been noticed if the news had not come shockingly, in double severity, that Nellie Flannery, who had just been confirmed and had come from the convent, had not only been married without so much as a word to her parents, but now was nowhere to be found. Grandmother, safely at sea under white sails that fascinated her, must have known surely the alarm she had caused, and she must have known, upon looking back to New England, that her leaving was forever.

She must have loved her husband very much and

been quite sure of him to forsake civilization for what she knew was a frontier. I never knew him, for he died before I was born, but I know he was tall and very strong, and likewise, strongly Irish. He was quietly gentle at home and given to recording his experiences and reflections in the backs and margins of books, which were written with care as though he were trying to leave something that stood for him when he was gone. Further than that, though, I guess without promptings at what sort of man he was, for Grandmother did not mention him often.

I doubt that Grandmother fell in love in the impulsive manner of the phrase. That would have meant a certain surrender to her emotions, which would have been impossible for Grandmother. She must have looked at him with detachment, as much detachment as she could summon at the moment, to decide that he was strong and good and gentle, and that, therefore, she was fond of him. Yet the decision was a hasty one, for they were married when she was sixteen and a week away from the convent and he was making the most of twenty-two. I said it was impulsive, but she explained that they really did know each other more than slightly, having met two weeks before they went away.

They went away without warning, because Grandmother always disliked explaining herself, as though her actions needed to be justified, and a wedding at the time, when she was a week away from the convent, would have taken elaborate explanation. Not only that, but there would have had to be an extended engagement, a trousseau, and a hope chest, along with lengthy admonitions and instructions from relatives. Grandmother dislikes such fuss and bother, and especially does she dislike displays of emotion. Having decided she loved the man, she wanted to marry him and get the anxiety over with.

My grandmother is enthusiastic about marriage and thinks there is something that can be said for love. The use of love in life has been overdone, of course. One doesn't have a husband sent down from heaven. Love comes from admiration and respect and sympathy. Grandmother will admit there are some people who are emotionally immature and there's no accounting for their love. But as a rule one can depend upon love.

Grandmother must have been from the start an expert in such emotional matters; either that, or she was exceptionally fortunate, recognizing the man who was to be her husband as easily as she did. For she had been cloistered in the convent since she was six and, except for her brothers and her brothers' friends and a gardener she waved to once, she knew no other man until she met her husband. She told me, since my questions had been exasperating, that her husband was the first man she had met when she came from the convent: therefore she had married him at once, as a good convent girl would. But I can't quite believe it of Grandmother.

I suppose he was the first man, at least the first likely man. But I imagine Grandmother questioned him first, and that the questioning was very severe.

Grandmother once explained why she was first attracted to him; not that she had meant to explain herself, for that would not have been like Grandmother. The explanation came disguised as philosophy, and most of her philosophies came while she was baking bread. She was baking in the range and had already poked tentative straws into the white bread, when I asked why she went to such bother when she could buy bread for ten cents a loaf. Grandmother regarded the question as absurd.

"Of course," she said, "bread can be bought; but one never knows whose hands have rolled it, or what has gone into it, for that matter. Besides, young man, I like to bake bread."

There was, it seems, a satisfaction in it. Not only a physical satisfaction, but a spiritual, yes, even a poetic satisfaction to it. It wasn't practical. "A young man of sixteen," she said, "is certain to be a poet, but a girl of sixteen—she is first a business woman."

Grandmother was evidently a business woman when she first looked at Grandfather, and he was as evidently a good investment. Indeed, he must have been a bargain with his intelligence and strength and his determination to chip off part of the world for his own.

But as a business woman, Grandmother was something of a speculator. While she wanted security for her future, she could speculate now. In New England she had security, and it seemed to get nowhere.

In the West, though, there was gold and insecurity and a promise. And even if her husband didn't have an income, he was likely to have one, when the two of them found where the gold was, to take some and build a home for a foundation for a family that would go on after they were gone, but would still be part of them.

Virginia City must have been a wild place then. Shacks were being torn down for stone and frame homes. The streets were narrow and dusty and crowded with men. Lines of prairie schooners, interrupted now and then with a stagecoach, waited while teamsters unloaded mining machinery and halves of beef. The town at the time, in the eighteen-sixties—and it has stayed the same since—was laid out lengthwise on the down side of Mt. Davidson. The mountain has a height of nearly eight thousand feet, and the height of Virginia City above sea level is from five to six thousand feet. The railroad curled in from the north and came to the center of the city. The city itself was perhaps seven miles long and continued to the Divide, the highest point, from which it dwindled down to Gold Hill, which was the south end of the Comstock Lode.

In the sixties the city was crowded with houses, pressed closely together as if for protection. In those days there were only eight main streets running north and south, but hundreds of streets running east and west. The long streets were called by the alphabet while the short, intervening streets, had such designations as Glory Climb and Puff and Pant Grade. These short streets ran right up the side of the mountain, and the tops of some of them could be reached only by foot or horseback. The roads of all streets were dirt, but the better streets had board sidewalks, even though wood cost a silver dollar an armful.

The homes changed between the sixties and the seventies from shacks and tents to two-story places that sometimes had French windows with green blinds and a porch with white pillars beneath a veranda. The door plates were usually of silver, that costing the least, while the wealthy went in for gold and even bronze door plates, bronze being the most expensive and elegant of all.

The yards in front were invariably small and usually well kept, considering the high price of water, which was one dollar a week for the house and one dollar for the garden. So the gardens had to be preciously kept, especially if one had a crab-apple tree, which was luxury, although the tree was sure to be stunted in such rarefied air. All the homes had fences, as indeed did most of the hotels; and the fences were always whitewashed. The interiors of the homes, too, were much alike, their owners going in for hair sofas and cane-bottom chairs, rocking chairs with cushion and shawl, and a wall paper that was likely to be domineering.

The public buildings were preferred in a color of furious red. The depot hung on the edge of town like a danger signal. The waiting room, too, was in red, and the benches were hastily painted planks that were not only hostile but treacherous with splinters. The fire house on B Street, well up the steep side of Mt. Davidson, had been likewise painted red, although the sleeping quarters had never been painted at all. These were in the loft and were for the paid firemen. The unpaid firemen had comfortable clubrooms, and if you were a person of importance you could meet in the clubrooms with the unpaid firemen. The main floor was the exhibit room, decorated with trophies and trumpets of silver which hung on all sides in glass-enclosed cases. The lower floor, on the down side of the mountain, was the barn and wagon room containing polished engines and triumphant hose hawsers. The horses were arranged in stalls on the lower floor in such a manner that they could be harnessed before the engines and then driven straight down the hill to the city.

It was the pride of the fire department, according to a contemporary, that the captain could blow a little whistle in Virginia City that would awaken the firemen on B Street and have engines, apparatus, and all at his side as soon as the wagons and—I presume— the horses could roll down the hill.

The saloons were every fourth door on C Street, and C Street was the principal street. There were saloons for all classes, and they ran in respectability from the Hangdog Bar, where whiskey could be mixed with a shudder, to the Crystal Saloon, where gentlemen met. The saloons of the Comstock rose to elegance in the Crystal, for it had gigantic chandeliers of cut glass and silver that hung menacingly from gold stanchions and a bar that was made of marble, although the foot rail was of the customary brass. The wall opposite the bar was hung with heavy gilt frames that had scenes in them from fistic encounters, especially the encounters of Irishmen with mustaches. There were prints, too, of crews of prize miners, men who could dig ten feet where their brothers dug eight and men who could "smell ore in rock." These valuable miners were depicted with their arms crossed to display their biceps, all deadly serious gentlemen and decidedly self-conscious with bold mustaches and forelocks. Naturally, they all were in undershirts. That was the uniform of the able-bodied workingman. The paintings were in the reds and brighter blues, with here and there a dash of yellow. They contained other serious gentlemen in banquet at such places as the Hoffman House, each guest in evening dress and smoking a certain brand of cigar that was advertised on a copper placard at the bottom of the painting. Alongside the walls of the saloon were large and intricate, not to say confusing, slot machines for pieces of four and eight bits. There was a phonograph, too, that stood out in the open of the room without benefit of cabinet. It played for two bits, and as it played one could see its wheels go around. The recordings were on copper and were usually the recording of some tenor.

But when Grandmother came to Virginia City, the town was yet to have its elegance. There were saloons, of course; but they were nothing to be proud of yet. Indeed, Virginia's one point of pride, as Mark Twain said, was that it had a cemetery already, for the bodies of its first twenty-six dead, all of whom had been murdered.

Grandmother's coming to town was an event, and one that made Grandfather apprehensive. The first night at the hotel many men found reasons to visit him and stare with wonder at his wife, who was then a small, dark-haired woman, almost seventeen but in hoop skirts and high collar, a very fragile-looking person with her very light skin and sensitive and youthfully serious face. The town was accustomed to pioneer women who were big women, often on the gaunt side, with strong faces and rough hands; and I suppose the prostitutes then were as flabby and expressionless as ever.

That night when the confused guests were gone, and Grandmother and her husband were in bed, they could hear outside in the streets the shouting and fighting of a pioneer mining town as it prepared to greet midnight. Because in those days the beginning of day found men dead in the streets without logical reason, and without apparent concern of the survivors, Grandfather brought his bride as soon as he could to the Divide, where they could be above Virginia and Gold Hill, up above the clamor. And he built a fence around his home that a marauder would find difficult indeed to pass, and after darkness came he never let his wife be home alone.

They had come to Virginia City in the year of

Mark Twain's arrival, in 1862. It was the season in spring just before the first families came, the people who were to be more or less permanent and not transgressors, like the prospectors. The prospectors looked upon the migration with the suspicion that these bewildered yet determined-looking settlers were intentionally bringing civilization with them. It was strapped in their prairie schooners, it was in the boxes that bulged in the stagecoaches, it protruded from the blanket rolls and boxes of utensils, and it was plain to see in the faces of children. If there were children, civilization was with them, and that in time would mean the end of swindling and renegade whites. The families were warned to go on to California, for the altitude here, they were told, would shrivel the lungs of the children and kill the cattle. But the families mostly stayed, and for the prospectors Virginia City became almost as unendurable as any other place.

The first few letters from Grandmother that came East by coach and pony express were neither descriptive nor intimate. She wrote little of her husband and herself, except to mention that their health was all right under the circumstances, and that a silly custom of the town prevented her from walking in the street alone, even in daytime. She noted that the streets were unbelievably dirty, despite the wind; that these men were drinking heavily, as men away from home will, and that traffic blockades of teams and wagons sometimes held for hours.

Grandmother said that Virginia City received its name from a local reprobate who called himself James Finney or James Virginia, depending upon which came to mind at the moment.

"But everyone knew," she said, "that his right name was James Fenimore, after the author. Unfortunately for his impressive fabrication, he weakened to exaggeration under spirits. They say his Southern idiom became more obvious and that he especially boasted about his home place, which was somewhere in the state of Virginia. At any rate, he was quick with words, was Mr. Finney Fenimore, or whoever he was. One night he named the city when he fell down in C Street and rolled to D Street. His bottle of whiskey was broken, but he kept the remains clasped to his breast as he sympathized with himself, saying over and over again, 'Poor old Jimmy Virginia.' I believe he also remarked that his heart was broken, so he decided that the tragedy should be noted. He named the scene and the city 'Jimmy Virginia.'

"I know that the circumstance seems implausible, but it fast became a legend; that's the way legends are."

In whatever circumstance, Jimmy Virginia, despite

his behavior, was a person of first importance on Comstock hill. He was a *nabob*, which is the miner's word for a capitalist. He could buy whiskey for his friends, and people who found it prudent to be agreeable, began referring to the settlement, in his presence, at least, as "Jimmy Virginia City." But they would say it with more meter than that. It would be "Jimmy Virginia City, me bhoys aroo." After such effort, whiskey had to follow, of course.

"Flannery," Grandmother said, speaking of her husband, "heard that Jimmy's interests were worth five million dollars, but that he seemed to be unable to realize any actual money. Each day his holdings became more valuable, but he must have become very tired of being a millionaire in name only, for on another evening that spelled a legend he sold the lot of his interests to Comstock himself for a bottle of whiskey, a blind horse, and a very worthy silk handkerchief."

Grandmother said it was pleasant to watch the legend of Jimmy Virginia increase in weight as his name and his interests accumulated awe, until Jimmy himself became a hero instead of the drunken and dirty little man who had gone on to other prospecting quarters with a comrade's knife driven well into his back.

For the most part, these early prospectors came to sudden ends; and even though they were in Nevada for money, they spent it foolishly. In those days, in the Civil War time, a traveler found that his scrip was scoffed at in the Comstock. His money had to be in gold or silver dollars, and for change he received "bits." To begin with these were actually bits of a dollar, being pieces broken off the coin by the assay or the blacksmith, and sometimes bitten off by the store-keepers. Later the bits became coins. The *short bit* was worth twelve cents; the *long bit*, worth fifteen cents; *two bits* were twenty-five cents; *four bits* were fifty cents; and *eight bits* were worth a dollar. Nothing cost less than a *short bit*, and articles that were worth only that much were generally given away, anyway. Even now in Nevada there is little currency and probably no pennies.

Not until after the Civil War when Nevada had become a state because of Abraham Lincoln's pleadings, for Comstock Lode could help pay the nation's debt abroad—not until then did the timid feel it safe to visit Virginia City. The Comstock had been regarded with complete disapproval. The people were too impulsive for the rest of the nation. There was that war incident, for one thing. Nevada had greeted the war with celebrations. Almost every man volunteered, but unfortunately just as many volunteered to fight for the South as for the North. Saloons flying the Confederate colors were as well patronized as those that flew the Federal flag, and enthusiastic friends met to find they had joined different armies. But that didn't matter, really; for it was still a sight to warm a man to see the volunteers singing and calling to friends to join in, as they marched up the street, side by side, the colors of the Yankees and the Rebels floating in the same breeze.

It took only a few days to settle the difficulty. After a speech or two from garrison commanders, in which it was pointed out that the Confederate speakers represented a land that was a long way off, everyone enlisted in the Northern army, that being the handier.

With this kind of precedent, people from California and the East were suspicious of Virginia City. Professional men came to the Comstock reluctantly. It was really the actors who followed after the miners. Theatrical companies which had been coming across the continent to San Francisco, extended their routes to include Virginia City. Howard's Theatre was there, almost from the first, but it used local players. Topliffe's Palace came late in '62; Maguire's, in '63. The important theatre, though, turned out to be Piper's Opera House. It was there that Piper took the profit, provided there was profit, and John Mackay paid the losses, if he could attend on Piper's passes.

Like many of the early opera houses, Piper's had a balcony shaped like a horseshoe, with four boxes on each side just above the stage. There was at the back a Pigpen and above that a Nigger Heaven, while downstairs were the loges, the Diamond Horseshoe and the Popular Seats. Piper's was lighted to begin with by candles, and later by oil lamps. These hung from large chandeliers which could be lowered to the floor for refilling. The footlights were oil lamps, too, that extended out to the audience on an apron that every once in a while would catch fire and singe the Dress Circle. The curtain, too, often ignited. It was usually a canvas with a brave mural on it that depicted Mt. Davidson in its glories, with at its height, just below the American flag and above the snow-capped peak, a large advertisement, entirely out of proportion, which said: "Fred's Livery Stable, Hay and Grains."

On a noteworthy evening when John Mackay brought Grandmother and her husband to see an actress she thinks was Modjeska, Grandmother met Mark Twain. He was seated in the very first row, in defiance of the footlight-apron, along with other employees from the newspaper, and protected from obscurity by an ornate and very red sign behind his chair which declared that these front-row seats were "Reserved for *The Enterprise*."

Between the acts, John Mackay, the patron of Nevada arts and stockholder in the mines, presented

Mark Twain to Grandmother with the flourish and rhetoric of the Hoffman House. "Mr. Samuel Clemens," he said, in part, "one of our ambitious and go-getting young scribes of our state's thriving journalism." Mr. Clemens bowed deeply with a reasonable amount of success for such a vigorous young man who was handicapped by being dressed in starched shirt front and cutaway coat. He was solicitous and wanted to know if Mrs. Flannery had been depressed too much by the drama's inconsiderate spirit. Mrs. Flannery replied that she had not yet had the opportunity to be depressed at all because the gentleman who was seated ahead of her had allowed her only fleeting glimpses. John Mackay, wounded but still gallant, offered hastily to have the gentleman beheaded and in that truncated condition run from the city on a rail.

The young critic suggested clemency for the offender and asked the privilege of escorting Mrs. Flannery to a seat in the newspaper section. Mrs. Flannery accepted. Bows again were given, apologies were offered, and Grandmother, with her hoop skirts and bustle, was placed in the front row alongside William Wright, who signed himself Dan De Quille, and a startled young man whose name, as Grandmother remembers it, was Peabody. The young man later found gold and leased a good deal of the south of France.

Grandmother that evening was told the hazards of being an editorial worker on the *Enterprise*. The newspaper would suffer no copy editors—or a change of copy, for that matter; each man wrote his story and placed it on a spindle. The printers picked it up from there. Yet, while each man could write as he pleased, he was entirely responsible for what he had written. A reader could learn immediately the name of the editor—each reporter called himself the editor—who wrote the article that offended him, and he was at privilege of speaking to the man about it. Most newspapermen, for that reason, were large men, familiar with rough and scuffle and the advantages of carrying a revolver.

The newspaper was especially proud of its criticism of the drama. An opening company faced not one critic, but four or five, all from the *Enterprise*. Each critic wrote a review and then voted which review should be published. If the play had been extraordinarily offensive or each review conceited, then four or five reviews were published. Grandmother recalls that after Walter Montgomery read three reviews, side by side, of his *Hamlet*, with each one indignant at length, he left Virginia City that very day and never again returned.

The *Enterprise* flourished until the dull summer of '93, to expire one day without warning. Its building is among the few that still stand in Virginia City. By now it is distinguished by an engraved message on its door, a masterpiece of understatement, which begins: "In this building, Mark Twain, who greatly enriched the Literature of the West . . ."

Writers never meant much to Nevada, for Nevada has always been too close to the earth to listen to literature. The state stands there, with its mountains and valleys and deserts, waiting to be developed by the physical labor of its people; and the people, working in its raw magnificence, do not care to read and write.

Grandmother regards literature as deficient, anyway; for it never comes when it is most needed, and it is seldom effective in a life that is rapidly moving. There is writing for entertainment and writing of yesterday's happenings, but there is no reflective writing, she thinks, until there is recollection.

Virginia City, Grandmother knows, had nothing to reflect upon. It came without precedent, and nothing like it will come again. It had no past and no future. It came; then it was gone.

But it was lively while it lasted. Such exciting days those were, in the sixties and seventies, with each stagecoach bringing new citizens; miners and gamblers, prostitutes and actors, sports and bandit chiefs, lawyers and capitalists, bringing all to Virginia. Life flowed swiftly. There were drinking bouts that passed importantly under the name of banquets, and there were banquets that were feasts, and for afterward there was The Line, where the whores were.

Sometimes the city would designate a day for public entertainment. The mines would agree to close together so that one company would not get ahead of another, the day would be declared a holiday, and all workingmen would put one day's wages into an entertainment fund. If six mines were active, which was usual, they used three shifts of men a day, with each shift having some five hundred men, the average wage being five dollars a day; then the entertainment fund would have almost fifty thousand dollars. That money would purchase the town for a day. San Francisco would be invited to Virginia City. Everyone in San Francisco who was a union man, and therefore a "good felly", would be requested to bring himself and his family to the Big Bonanza. The San Francisco citizens, having perhaps successfully crossed the Sierras, were met at the Virginia City depot by bands, excited children, and an impressive reception committee, each official wearing a badge on his lapel and holding a derby in his hand.

Miners scrubbed themselves, dressed in suits that were seldom seen except on Sunday, arranged ribbon ties, and still wearing their heavy shoes, for the streets were dusty, walked down to the depot with their families.

It was a holiday, and cigars were smoked. The important people arrived in buggies, with the horses still smelling of soap. The politicians unwisely came in carriages that had silver stanchions and their horses had bits wrought from gold pieces. In town, the bachelors were already at the bar. Their coats were soon off, for the sun was high and the morning was warm, and under their suspenders their silk shirts were beginning to stick to their skin. The street was lined with horses, drawn near the troughs, and their long noses were in the green water. Hotels flew the Star Spangled Banner and the Golden Bear. Gamblers counted on a good day and had their tables stacked high with dollars. Band stands and speakers' stands were hung with bunting, and butcher shops had meat hanging out front, proudly, with the chops decorated with artificial flowers and with at least one display in carefully wrought veal of the American flag. Firecrackers were for sale in Chinatown, and on C Street there wasn't a store but that had "WELCOME" on it.

At eight o'clock in the morning, when the train approximately arrived, having been on the road since the morning before, the bands were ordered to be ready. As the train came out of the tunnel triumphantly, orange and copper in the sunlight, the music

blasted and the San Franciscans were greeted with
cheers; and even if the residents of the city didn't
know each other, they shook hands heartily anyway
and promptly formed a parade to march down C
Street.

If the heavens were just they would be clear that
day, as the parade passed through Virginia City. First
came the military companies, the Emmet Guards and
the Nevada Guards, marching with their matching
companies from California, each company in full
dress of blue and gold, each man with white gloves
and with a sword, too, for some reason.

Then came the Masons, in every gorgeous order of
them. The Knights Templars followed, to be followed in turn by the Order of Red Men. It was understood, of course, that the Order of Red Men, an organization of extreme importance, had nothing in
common with the Piutes who stood on the sidewalk,
watching the parade go by. Regalia of all orders were
trimmed with gold and silver, with bullion fringe and
lace to match, and all orders were distinguished by
heavy badges. Only the Miners' Union, which spon-
sored the day and was the strongest group in town,
was without uniforms. But the union men did have
badges a foot long that flowed from their lapels. The
heroic firemen, the pride of the city, followed the
miners, squadrons of them marching impressively be-

fore their shining wagons, each paid or unpaid fire-
man carrying a silver trumpet, and each silver trumpet held in its horn a bouquet of artificial flowers, the
flowers, of course, in red, white, and blue.

Indeed, artificial flowers were everywhere, for they
were rarer and harder to get than the common wild
blossoms of cactus and sagebrush, which spread a
bright carpet over the mountain sides.

The fire wagons had magnificent nickel smoke-
stacks which reflected the dignity of the silver-gray
fire horses; and in each nickel smokestack was a young
lady, elected to her position by ballot, who was attired
as the Goddess of Liberty, with a paint-topped torch
in her hand and yard of white crêpe around her. After
the fire wagons came the battalion of flag-bearers,
holding aloft silk flags that represented all nations—
that is, all nations whose flags had been published in
the dictionary. A miner standing on a float carried by
his fellows was dressed to represent Columbus, "although it might be," Grandmother said, "that Chris-
topher Columbus didn't have a mustache like Flannery's."

The school children were in the parade, led by the
girls' choir singing "My Country, 'Tis of Thee," and
directly behind the children and fascinating them so
that they walked along with their heads turned back,
was a printing press on wheels, throwing out papers

as it was carried along. A rolling quartz mill came next, and then a float that was supposed to be the interior of a mine, with miners with faces scrubbed clean drilling into a pasteboard boulder.

There were cheers from one end of C Street to the other. It was a wonderful day. And once in a while a prospector would have his heart warmed by a sight so stirring; unable to constrain himself and his morning's whiskey, he flung quartz specimens in which there was gold and silver to his scrambling audience of Indians. When his specimens were gone, he began with short bits thrown to children, for an Indian wouldn't want money; then, for lack of dimes, he threw pieces of two bits and even of four bits, with the cheer and heavy approval of his comrades.

Since the town was purchased by the union fund, money was worthless on a holiday anyway. Money that couldn't be used immediately was cumbersome to a man who had no family responsibility. Of course, no *respectable* miner would throw away money or pick it up, either, even if it were thrown at his feet. Indeed, if bits landed too often beside him, there would be trouble and fists and apologies. Nor would he allow *his* children to scramble for it. The guests from San Francisco, though, had no such complicating scruples. They would break from the ranks and with cries of prosperity wrestle for the scattered coins, while the

Comstock men looked on, ashamed for them and embarrassed. Finally, a constable would be forced to lead away the prospector who had been unsociable enough to break up a fine parade.

Anyone in town could go into any saloon—that is, any gentleman—and order what he pleased without cost; or in any restaurant, hotel, or whatever souvenir stores were open. Barbecue pits were dug along A Street every hundred yards or so, and barbecue tables ran the length of the town, up and down hill. There were pigs and sheep roasted. Quarters of beef turned on spits, vegetables baked in the ashes. Trout wrapped in leaves were baked or fried with bacon. Catfish from Washoe Lake were there, too, for they were something of a delicacy. And there were crates of freshly baked bread, and likewise crates of apples that had come for the occasion from as far away as Placerville. There were speeches, too, in the same proportion, great, lengthy, eloquent speeches by hired speakers, in which the clauses curled around and around and came out in favor of union labor.

"I can understand," Grandmother wrote, "the enthusiasms for strength on such holidays, for Comstock miners, with their supple muscles, can easily win such matches as tug-of-war and shoveling. But I cannot understand why there is emphasis on fleetness, for the Californians always win the foot races and win them quite easily, too. It invariably causes a slight bitterness, for Nevada people resent their guests winning all the races. It is not very polite. In defense there is always at the last, a squaw race, with stout Piute women waddling furiously in their bright patches. The guests, however, don't seem to mind such satire."

Grandmother had not intended to see Virginia's first feast day. It seemed to her that the plans were in the hands of the wrong element. But in the early morning of the day her husband awakened her with excitement. He was dressed and shaved to the blood already, and he implored her to hurry, please, or they wouldn't see the train come in. While she was having breakfast, her neighbors hurried by her house toward the road to the depot, holding their fine skirts a little higher than the dust. Musicians trotted by anxiously, clutching their instruments, and children were calling wildly to one another. Her husband came into the kitchen again, this time wearing his hat, to warn her the train was already due. Then she likewise hurried, and half ran down the hill to the depot, which was not very much like Grandmother.

Chapter Three

Chapter Three

I SUPPOSE THAT WHEN GRANDMOTHER REFLECTS UPON THE YEARS OF HER LIFE those things of her youth must seem very far away; so far, in fact, that they may have happened to some one she knew. Recalling three-quarters of a century must be tiring indeed, particularly tiring since the events of her life, the building of her home and the first years of her marriage and the births of her children, had been in an age that was actually gone and in a city that no longer existed. It had been a rough, eager city in a new land with a life much in length like Grandmother's. Virginia City and Grandmother met when they were young and they became old together. Her husband had died in this wild new land, and now even his grave was gone. He died in a winter when the snow had piled high against the bedroom windows, but so many years have passed since then that not even the winters are the same. They are milder, and the snowdrifts that sometimes came completely over the house are now farther north. A neighbor once clung all night to the chimney top of her house, unable to find his way home in the storm, but recalling that now, in these rainy winters, would make it seem scarcely believable.

While he was dying, Grandfather regretted he was leaving his wife in a wild land. He wanted her safely in the East with her children, for it did not seem then that Virginia City would ever be a peaceful place; indeed, that in time to come it would settle down to die and vanish. The years he lived in Virginia City were his best years, as they were Virginia City's best years, from the middle sixties to the late eighties; and while he was dying, the wealth of the Comstock Lode was finally realized. Prospectors still became fabulously wealthy and did not know what to do with their money except that they wished to buy whiskey for the town, and castles in Europe for the brides they could now select.

Financial matters were more turbulent than ever; railroads and coach lines were busy with families hurrying toward the Bonanza and brokers traveling anxiously back and forth from San Francisco to Virginia City. Restlessness from the Civil War lingered among many of the disbanded service men, who had been trained to fight but no longer had a foe, and maintained regiments anyway against an enemy they had not yet determined. There was fighting in the mines, though; not for soldiers but for workers. Labor struggles were furious with shooting and knifing. The Miners' Union was reorganizing, and squads of miners, demanding better working conditions, were barricading the drifts, refusing to work or to let anyone work until the tunnel levels were timbered for strength against cave-ins. But the veins of gold and silver were so rich to follow that mining companies did not want to hesitate for protection. They were satisfied to abandon a vein at two or three thousand feet below the surface, for the machinery was yet to be invented that would allow miners to go as far as five miles into the earth and work beside boiling water and rocks so hot that to touch them meant to be scalded.

In Grandfather's time, the miners worked in rapid shifts without benefit of cooling systems, the crews in the lower levels working hard for twenty minutes or a half-hour and then sprinting to a higher, cooler level. The mines were series of tunnels, each tunnel running like a hallway, with the mines themselves like submerged office buildings, the floors or levels connected by a form of elevator which was called a "hoist" or "bucket."

Later, in the early nineteen-hundreds, pieces of machinery would be lowered into the mines and built into great drilling mills that would be capable of cutting great streets thousands of feet under the surface, extending farther than even the length and breadth of Virginia City. But before the century, the mining that the city was so proud of was really crude in comparison to what it would be in the next decade. Men worked naked, and were so often overcome with heat that not many of them lived past forty. The levels were run with rats, and the air down there was so close and hot that if a rat was accidentally killed, the nearest miner had to hurry it to the surface or the air would become so bad that no man could breathe it.

But Grandfather liked mining and he liked Virginia City. The impact of living hard fascinated him. He was taking hold of life with both hands, and he grasped it as though he could not get it close enough. He had none of Grandmother's detachment; nor could he see her horizon. He had the strength and vitality for active life, and he loved the world most when it offered a challenge. While Grandfather was willing to fight everyone at once, he would not allow the combats to disturb his home. Home he used as a sort of sanctuary and safety zone. Here he retreated to rest for a moment, beside Grandmother, before he marched out to combat the world again. He regarded Grandmother as a fragile and tender person he must protect every minute; himself, he could get along in this tough, rough world, but his wife—he thought she was too fragile for it. And Grandmother must have decided it was best that he did think so.

Grandfather looked upon marriage as the only proper relation for a man. It was right, just as anything else was wrong. Bachelors were undependable, husbands were good men, and fathers were best. Children were a duty and a joy; at least, they were a duty, and that first; if they were also a joy, it was just that much the better. But there had to be children, for the population must be replenished, and with Grandfather that was a personal responsibility. For that matter, most of the rules for society's conduct were his responsibility. His share had to be done. After he set the example, others could do as they pleased, provided they didn't transgress on his rights. He was a man, he maintained, who did as he was supposed to do; and in return for all this effort, he expected to be considered with the respect due a citizen and a father.

Grandfather realized that his beliefs were the right ones, and that anyone who lived by others was either slipshod or a Republican. His side was the right side; the other half was all wrong. While he was not always in the majority, he was in the right, just the same. He would have been indignant if he had been accused of dogmatism. Why, anybody could see that he knew what he was talking about; only a fool would disagree. He was stubborn, perhaps, but what difference did that make?

Grandfather thought his wife was entirely too tolerant. Her beliefs were subject to change and she would admit, sometimes, that she was wrong; and if she were certainly wrong, she didn't seem to be disturbed about it. Grandmother was willing to be lenient of Mrs. Matthews, who was an old gossip, and malicious, too, as everybody knew; and Grandmother would trade with a butcher who had cheated her, and she smiled in reply when men who did not belong to the Miners' Union tipped their hats to her. She did not seem to realize that non-union men were her enemies. That seemed such an obvious weakness in his wife, Grandfather was often infuriated. He believed in the direct blow: Crush your enemies before they crush you. And here was his wife being kind to them. A butcher that cheated her once would cheat her again. Grandfather thought that Grandmother should learn things like that. But she never did. Grandfather realized the failure was no doubt because she was a woman and nearer to God than he; nevertheless, God and he had better collaborate for her protection.

Although Grandfather was well aware of his responsibilities, his burden did not seem to restrict his enjoyment of living. Under his logic, in fact, the bigger the burden the better. He believed in working hard and playing hard, until, without his knowing it, work and play became the same. He especially liked to sing, and he did sing rather well, being prejudiced for those vehement songs that allowed him free use of his arms. He joined groups that sang together, and he insisted upon bringing Grandmother to all the recitals.

Grandfather remained a sociable man, gregarious and social-conscious, provided he kept the impression that all his friends were very much like him. If they held his ideals, he gloried in their triumphs, suffered with their defeats, and stood by them in their calamities. He was always enthusiastically gregarious, and he was never more of an agitated altruist than the night he fought the fire that destroyed Virginia City.

The fire started early one morning in the summer of 1872 by an overturned lamp in a boarding house on A Street, in the shabby part of town, where the buildings were built against one another and even atop one another on the down side of the hill. The fire ran freely, spreading on to C Street to burn down the north of Virginia, and before it finished took away some twenty thousand buildings and cost the city ten million dollars.

The fire was impossible to control, for most of the buildings were of wood and the state had been without rain. The reservoir had a low level of water and the sagebrush was dry and loose in the wind. The clouds of smoke formed into a menacing pyramid, and the people awakened in terror, some of them running in the streets in their nightshirts and underclothes, not knowing which way to go, for the flames seemed to come from all sides. People fled in their buggies, with blinders over the eyes of the horses. The horses in the corrals were crying and kicking against the fences, and one of them burst through and ran terrified to the mountain.

With other men from the mine, Grandfather organized the townspeople to make a fire break. The equipment in the fire department was useless against so huge a fire. Although the paid and unpaid firemen worked hard, in their shining helmets and black belts, to hitch the frightened horses, they were unsuccessful. And their streams of water evaporated into steam as they struck the fire.

Grandfather and the volunteers formed a fire break by dynamiting buildings in the path the fire had indicated. While the flames swept nearer the Divide, horses were run hooded from barns, dynamite was placed in the cellars of houses, and then, with a shout of warning, homes and barns exploded. Streets of homes were dynamited, a block at a time, but the flames leaped hundreds of feet to clear the breaks and roar on triumphantly.

Indians, dragging and kicking their ponies, clambered up the side of Mt. Davidson and stood near the top breathlessly watching while the city disappeared below them in volumes of smoke. Crowds of refugees, carrying what possessions they could, climbed to the comparative safety of the ore hills. It was characteristic that the Indians should choose the mountains while the settlers clung to the remnants, at least, of civilization. On the ore hills the women waited with their children, while the men with their older sons, whose eyes must have been shining, joined the dynamiters who faced the fire.

It was an exciting day for Grandmother, being awakened by the anxious fire bells. Her house echoed the bumping wheels of fire wagons and the roar of horses' hooves. Mine whistles blew in frustration and until the last moment, when the flames struggled over the barren heaps of discarded ore to leap into the mines themselves. Caches of dynamite exploded; and even the refugees had to laugh when the little armory went off like firecrackers. Grandmother had time to take most of the family's belongings to a large hill of milled ore where there was nothing to burn. She hurried back and forth, followed by all the Piute children she could commandeer, every one carrying armfuls of clothing and dropping some of it, too, to leave a trail between house and hill. She salvaged the chickens, and saved the doves, nests and all. Then with her hands protecting her stinging forehead Grandmother stood very tired on the hill, with the Piutes squatted around her, watching when the smoke lifted to see where her husband could be, while the fire down below took homes away in a breath.

The fire never reached the peak of the Divide. It marched up and down C Street like an angry warrior, but the buildings in its intended path had been blasted away, and when the wind turned slightly, the fire was sent up the side of Mt. Davidson. The Divide was an island above a sea of ash, and the townspeople were tearful, looking down from the hillsides at what had been their homes.

"They all shared the same fate," said Grandmother, "and there was some comfort in that. They thanked God that they were alive and had lost only their homes. It could have been worse; that was reassuring. Flannery said that some of them immediately remembered fires that had been worse than this, while others even remembered fires in which no one at all had come out alive."

But after this fire, when families were reunited and it was discovered that no one of much importance had turned to ash, the citizens forgot in their common excitement exactly what had caused the despair. Their homes were gone, which meant there was a great deal of work to be done before nightfall. The lucky people on the Divide moved their belongings back into their homes and those whose homes were lost searched for abandoned mine tunnels, where they could sleep.

They could not stop talking about the fire, though. The sight had been magnificent. Even as they worked they shouted about it. Did they see that fat China-man running as fast as he could down A Street, without any clothes? And Wilson—they should have seen him, running from his precious saloon with all the brandy he could carry; and they should have seen the way the lads from the Norcross Mine swiped the brandy!

The grandeur of the fire infatuated the people. That first feeling of terror was gone. Fear had overwhelmed them that they had been stranded in a wild land, with civilization burned down behind them. But relief parties were already arriving. The curious came, too, attracted by the pyramid of smoke that could be seen even at Lake Tahoe, in California. The visitors had to be told in detail the thrill of having seen that fire burning.

By nightfall, when everyone had eaten, the Virginia City people gathered in the Miners' Union Hall in Gold Hill, and what was to have been a serious discussion of their future turned into a public dance. There was more food later, too, steaks eaten before the huge bonfires, with everyone singing and dancing.

"Your grandfather," Grandmother said, "sang the loudest of all. He certainly made a spectacle of himself that night, singing as loud as he could and waving his hands, dressed as he was in his burned and blackened clothes."

The pioneers were hardy and courageous, Grandmother had to admit. They had lost their possessions, to be sure, but what they had owned had been purchased with the gold, and there was still a lot more of that in the ground. Why, there was gold in the streets, they knew; but they were busy with veins of gold and couldn't be bothered with dust. They won Grandmother's respect that night after the fire, for the foolish impulsiveness that made them poor citizens also made them good pioneers; and in a common calamity, where they shared with each other, they became good citizens instead of just impulsive pioneers. That was significant to Grandmother.

She was amazed that Virginia City could be so rapidly rebuilt. From the first, the supplies had come generously. It was an age of confidence, and the bankers believed in the Comstock; they were willing not only to redevelop the mines but to lend enough money to build better homes. The rebuilding itself went on at all hours. In a few weeks the citizens were able to move down from their shacks on the mountain to their partially constructed houses. The mines operated again, and life in Virginia City came back to its routine.

The routine, though, was broken almost before it began, for it seems the gods were envious of such vigor in simple mortals and dispatched a punishment that took the form of a tornado that came over the Sierras, whistling its warning as it came; and the homes that had been so recently constructed and were not yet staunch, were blown to confusion. The town this time was indignant. The tornado was a personal insult; men walked about the streets in a daze, muttering. The tornado had not bothered the homes on the Divide, and this pointed the insult. Grandmother and the other residents felt almost ostracized, believing it would have been perhaps better if the tornado had hurt their homes a little, perhaps torn away a fence or brushed loose a shutter; but to disregard their homes completely was too obvious and divine a favor.

Rebuilding Virginia City again was a very difficult problem; now the Comstock district had no more trees for lumber. Wood in Virginia City was more expensive than its weight in flour, and almost its weight in gold. The mines, in the beginning, had cut most of the trees for timbering, but there never had been much lumber, anyway, for the altitude kept the trees stunted. There was more wood underground than there was growing in all of Nevada. Even firewood cost a dollar an armful, and it was chips and bark, sagebrush roots and the stumps of trees that the Chinese had uprooted.

But in time prairie schooners came loaded with timber, and trains—as many as forty-five a day—fought their way over the uneven, lurching single track from California. The trains brought carloads of workmen, too, and the clamor of mills cutting wood, men hammering and sawing, and the trains arriving, lasted night and day, despite the protests of the miners who contended that when they came home from their work they needed their sleep.

Until a year ago one of the original train engines was still running in Nevada. It had been the finest engine of all, for it had copper-plating; with the decline of the Comstock it pulled the only train that came to Virginia City. Its runs were once a day, back and forth to Reno, and toward the last it scarcely ever had a passenger but was maintained because of the mail. Grandmother said that every letter she received cost the government two bits, not only because there was not enough mail to keep a train running but because the engine was so ancient that parts could not be purchased for it but had to be especially manufactured; and the engine usually needed new parts. Just the same, the proud copper-plate on the engine was always gleaming.

The railway line was constructed before railroad

men understood the mathematics of grading, and the track wound around the Geiger Grade, not daring to try to climb the mountains. The track caused passengers to take four hours to travel from Reno to Virginia City, while by highway the distance was twenty-two miles, although by either highway or track the travel had to be at a thoughtful gait.

The engine was illustrated on postcards that could be purchased in the Virginia Confectionery. It was a very small engine with a copper smokestack that opened like a funnel. What it lacked in size and strength it gained in appearance, for it was proud and very shiny, with copper and steel carefully polished; and even its cowcatcher, which spread out in front like a hand, was copper-plated.

The scene on the postcard seemed to depict some sort of rite, with gentlemen with derbies and parted hair shaking hands with the engineer and firemen and looking toward the camera very pleased. Most of my interest in the card, though, was Grandfather, for he stood there holding his derby and wearing an expression that was grave and puzzled; indeed, a sort of polite stare. He was also wearing a short coat with many buttons and tight-legged trousers that seemed scarcely long enough. Of all the men, he was the one without a mustache. The picture must have been taken in the late eighties, for Grandfather was in middle life, and the occasion must have been fairly important because he was wearing his stock-board suit, and because he and Grandmother had been married twenty years before she could convince him he didn't need a mustache.

It was the custom in Virginia City for a respectable man to change from his mining clothes before he went down into town to look at the stock board. This was the period of financial speculation, and the city was cluttered with brokers. Their offices were in the buildings on C Street and their stock boards faced the sidewalk. The boards were of slate, and quotations were written on them in chalk; and schoolboys studied the principles of fancy handwriting to get jobs as stockboard markers. The writing on the boards was a script, the fancier the better, for the boards were a fashionable meeting place. Crowds generally gathered in the afternoon to form into dignified little groups. Friends gathered there as though by arrangement to talk stock and relate the day's anecdotes. Ladies attended in carriages handled by gentlemen, and sometimes they attended alone, for the boards were approved meeting places. Some of the ladies even had colored drivers in livery, but this was an extraordinary elegance that caused the disapproval of envy.

Mostly the carriages were drawn side by side so that the ladies could visit; and if the ladies descended to the street to shop in the New York Bazaar, they protected their complexions with tiny parasols, which they called "afternoon bumbrashoots." Yet some of the city's finest gentlemen chewed toothpicks thoughtfully, while they watched the boards, and those who were unmarried and able therefore to chew tobacco, were allowed to spit in the gutter, for the theory of sanitation was regarded as just so much more nonsense from France. Still, the trade boards were such a place as a lady would select for her promenade, especially if she had a style from an Eastern emporium, or if her husband had given her a new carbuncle pin.

Although the varying quotations on the stock boards meant money, there was not—as a rule—very much excitement among the people. By the late eighties much of the furious speculation among the townspeople was ended. The trading was between mining companies and curb men; it was organized, big finance by now, and the people who visited the boards of C Street were the small and cautious investors, who bought either bonds for security or stocks for small gambling.

In the seventies and in the early eighties, the gambling at the stock boards had been heavy. There were new mines beginning, and many new veins were being struck. Stock was cheap. Some of the stock in the wealthiest mines had been sold for a few dollars a share, for the same price, indeed, as stock for mines that turned out to be *wildcats*. Men and women and sometimes children bought shares of stock on margin without having the slightest knowledge of the stock that they were buying, and they would sell it back in the same day, much as a man might enter a poker game. If the stock went up, they took their profits and tried again; if the stock went down and their brokers called for "more mud," they either paid or forfeited. But in the late eighties and nineties values did not fluctuate so rapidly and the stock boards became a fashionable meeting place, considered to be as high-class as even the Crystal Saloon.

Most of the people around the stock boards were from the East, a generation or two removed from northern Europe. Those who were not Americans by birth were said to have come from the Old Country, whether it was Germany, France, or England. Everyone, though, considered himself something besides an American. He was a German or an Englishman. Yet there were certain times when talk turned to patriotism that a man was stoutly an American, and in the nineties, when a man declared that he was an American, he usually added he was "an American first, last, and all the time." That was as much of a definition as he could give. Of course, he knew that the Indians were Americans, too, but he would not admit they were the same kind of Americans that he and his friends were. Nor did he believe that the few immigrants from southern Europe were Americans. Perhaps they had been naturalized and perhaps even they could vote; but they were not Americans, they were Hungarians. Hunkies, they were, whether from Hungary or Italy.

The wealthy citizens and those who held all offices and got the good jobs were usually of German or Irish descent. Neither the Irish nor the Germans considered themselves prejudiced in their own favor. They simply felt they were superior people, and let it go at that. Other people were foreigners. Foreigners had swarthy faces and couldn't even speak English.

Except for a few Hungarians, the lower class was English, although the members insisted they were Cornish. They were well liked, the Cornishmen, and they were respected, for they were good hard-rock miners. Yet they were regarded with condescension and with friendliness called Cousin Jacks and Jinnies. They were believed to be inferior to the Germans and Irish because they were not born in the United States. The Germans and Irish had already been in America for all of a generation, but the Cornishmen had been brought directly from the British coal mines. Then, too, they had an accent, and no one who spoke with an accent was an American. This was four generations after the Declaration of Independence, and there were still some people living who had read the Constitution.

Most of the restaurants were operated by the Germans, who left their imprint on the Western appetite. From the first Grandmother seems to have been impressed with the Western appetite, for in one of her earlier letters she wrote:

"Most of the restaurants are frankly called 'eating houses' and are operated by German families of hearty descent. They offer meals of two kinds, the four-bit meal, which everyone refers to as the 'square meal,' and the two-bit meal, which is so unpopular it has no other name.

"For breakfast Flannery and I were offered eggs and bacon, small steaks, toast, wheatcakes (we call them pancakes), coffee and a dish of most helpful prunes. Flannery was delighted, but we were both astounded not only at the meal's size, but that fresh butter and eggs, besides the lean, could be procured in this mountain fastness.

"Dinner was an equal revelation; indeed, both dinner and supper included at least ten kinds of meat and ten or twelve vegetables. And the vegetables were fairly fresh! The meat must come from the cattle on the hillsides, but the vegetables from greener lands in Nevada and perhaps from California. I must mention, while I am so thoroughly at it, that there were four kinds of dessert, which is to say there were four kinds of pie.

"In this, an 'eating house,' one's table is family style, and all the courses are brought immediately; at the same time, even the four kinds of pie. The table becomes heaped. Only the coffee causes the waitress a second trip to table. The coffee is renewed through the meal, for everyone drinks a good deal of it. Flannery has turned as fond of it as he is of tea.

"We were told that it is only through urgent necessity that anyone would partake of a two-bit meal. It is practically starvation rations. Just two kinds of meats and only three vegetables, one dessert (no choice) one cup of coffee and two renewals. The limit of three cups seems a rigid rule, beyond compromise. Naturally, no one wishes to starve at the two-bit table; even the beggars in the streets request the price of a 'square meal.' "

Virginia City's really fashionable place for dinner was the International Hotel, a six-story brick building that cared for the visiting dignitaries; but it came later in the city's life, in the eighties. There a gentleman took his lady when he wished her an evening away from the kitchen. When Grandfather took his lady to the International dinner room—imagine, dinner at the end of the day!—his children remained at home. Children did not dine in the dinner room, but if their parents were living in the hotel they were allowed supper in their room.

The dinner room had the highest ceiling in the city, higher than even the belfry in the fire house, and people came often to look up at the ceiling, which was inlaid with a metal supposed to be gold and hung with massive glass chandeliers. The walls had thick, rich paintings of scenes in the English countryside. English countryside is the phrase because in the International House one never spoke of the Old Country. The silverware and cut glass were heavy and solid, but the dishes were china, except upon banquet occasions when, for a certain amount, the gold plates could be hired.

There were waiters instead of the widows who waited on table at the eating houses, and waiters had to be tipped. The ladies who waited on table would never consider accepting a gratuity. Indeed, in one of the restaurants where some one had attempted to tip, a lady had a sign saying: "No Appreciations—We Are Americans!" But the waiters in the International Hotel were French. Grandfather, for one, believed tipping was a strictly French custom, and regarded himself as a man of the world when he left a Frenchman four bits.

Until I was older, my grandfather was more of a

character in Grandmother's anecdotes than a person who had once lived in our house. He was the picture on the postcard and the owner of a heavy gold watch that had heavenly blue hands and a snap cover with flowery designs and his initials engraved upon it. I heard, of course, how Grandfather had been crushed and burned in the mines, but that was before I was born and therefore long ago. Grandmother told of the humorous things that he did, but she seldom mentioned the accident.

She was not sure when she saw the ambulance coming and the men running after it that the ambulance wagon contained her husband. She thought it would be Frank, her eldest son, who had been to town that day; and she started to run to the gate when she remembered that they would be needing hot water. She ran back to the kitchen to put the kettle on the range. It was from there that she heard, as though it came from a long way, her husband's voice directing the men. She was so relieved then that she almost fainted because she knew that it was not Frank after all, but some one her husband had brought home who had been hurt in the mine. He had done that before, for Virginia City didn't have a decent hospital.

Even when the men carried him in, he was so badly scalded that Grandmother scarcely knew him. It was more of a scarecrow they were carrying than a man, for they had wrapped him in rags and blankets. He had refused to wait at the mine for the doctor; instead, he had to come home as soon as he could. He was blind already, but he was directing the men, telling them, "Easy, there," and how to open the storm door.

Grandfather felt better at home in his own bedroom, in his large bed, of which he was so fond. It had been built by his specifications to the size, almost, of two ordinary beds, but it was just right for him, and now he looked huge in it, swathed as he was in bandages. He even improved the first few days, and his big voice bounded throughout the house to keep the volunteer servants in a state of hurrying anxiety. In the long afternoons, when his wounds began pulling, he sang. It was absurd to tell Grandfather to be quiet and save his strength, for he was so badly hurt he knew he could not recover, and he knew no logical reason why he should save his strength; and being quiet hurt him so. If he had just lain there, waiting for himself to die finally, the house would have been hushed and his family would have waited quietly, too; and the strain of their fearful waiting would have been upon his wife.

Grandfather summoned his boys for lectures or to send them sprinting on errands. He told Frank to bring home ice cream every night and he told Albert to walk like a man, not to be tiptoeing around the house. He would allow no murmurs in the next room, where his friends were. He wanted them to speak up instead of just waiting.

By the day, though, it became increasingly certain that the people in the next room had come for a solemn occasion. In there with them was his youngest daughter, a very small child, and their partly suppressed anxiety and tireless reassurances frightened her so that Grandmother brought the child into the bedroom with Grandfather, where there was no anxiety apparent.

The doctor was cheerful. He admitted he could do little for Grandfather except try to ease the pain. Grandmother had called him to the case because he was young. The company doctor, an elderly man, had constantly reassured her that he was treating her husband in the safe, old-fashioned way, which had been to bleed him. Bleeding wouldn't help, Grandmother said. It just made Flannery weaker to face the pain. The young doctor at least let her husband smoke and have whiskey when he wanted it.

Grandfather lived that way for two weeks, seeing only light and dark, aware of his future and hoping that he would die in the daytime. During the morning a great beam of sunlight came in through the tall window and lay across his bed. It was all that he could see, but he said that he could see it so clearly that if he wanted to he could reach out and hold it. But in the afternoon the light retreated across the room, slowly and inevitably, and the family looked upon its going as though the last of life went with it.

These were the uneasy hours, and Grandfather stirred in his immense bed and muttered that some damn' thing was the matter with his confounded pillows.

"You must lie back," the doctor would say.

Grandfather grumbled about that, but the doctor and Grandmother would hold his shoulders, small hands upon his giant's back, and slowly lay him on the bed. It was painful; the skin would be tight.

He treated the young doctor with amused tolerance, calling him "Sonny" and threatening to come back and get him if he let him go at night.

"It's just that I want to see," he said. "I want to see where I'm going." And although he was joking, he meant what he said. But he had to laugh, even if others had to laugh with him, because he knew that every time he spoke seriously, his words were taken as absolute and final.

It was the late afternoons that were the hardest. Grandmother left him one evening, just before dusk, to stand out on the side porch, to watch the sun disappear beyond Mt. Davidson. The boards on the porch were stiff yet with winter and creaked as she walked.

Her shawl was drawn around her shoulders, and the wind that began to come up as the sun went down was already spreading its fingers in her hair.

She must have been still young that evening, and she must have had many hopes, for as the sunlight began to leave the hillside, she followed it to higher ground. She walked on through the shadows past the houses of her neighbors. It was the first time she had left the house in many days; she must have felt the ground underneath as she walked.

She walked on to where there were no more houses, beyond even the corrals, to the higher, rougher ground, to the very top of the Divide, where no pioneer had built his home because the weather was cruel there in all seasons. She stood on the highest point, where later a monument was erected to the Comstock Lode, and stood there like a symbol of herself, with her shawl drawn around her and her face to the last of the sun.

Below her were Gold Hill and Virginia City; but they were so far below, and the dark down there was already so deep, that she could see only the yellow glows of light in the kitchens of the houses as wives prepared supper for their husbands. Beyond the city and to her back was no horizon but darkness, with darker clumps of it where there was sagebrush.

But on the Divide there were still a few rays of the

sun. Snow covered Mt. Davidson, and nests of it were near her, in shelters where the wind had not yet managed to get it. Between Grandmother and the mountain was the valley of the Comstock, so dark it need not have been there. She and the mountain were alone in the light.

In her pride and emotion Grandmother felt that she could somehow detain the sun from falling, or persuade it not to set this evening. But even as she stood there, giving all her strength to the sun, it sank steadily. Just above the mountain, it seemed for a moment to linger. It seemed even to halt. And then it was gone. The wind was blowing now, and down below in the city lights appeared in the streets as the lamplighter walked from one post to another. Grandmother walked home in the dusk.

That night Grandfather died, in the dark while Grandmother was lying down on the big bed beside him.

Funerals can be merciful; their details are demanding. They make the ache dull and heavy, and through the preparation and burial Grandmother's heart beat like a drum slowly tapped with a finger.

But, for many days after, it was difficult for Grandmother to understand why her husband had been refused his last wish. She even doubted her sanity that evening on the hillside and wondered if she had been arrogant. But Grandmother has been here long enough now to see many hopes come to frustration. For a while she searched and could find no reason for her husband's passing, and then into these matters she enquired no longer.

In the years to come Grandmother found that calamities were always occurring to the good and the bad alike, and often at the same time; death could scarcely be reward and revenge in the same common blow. Sometimes for everybody the most approved laws were contradicted; sometimes even the acknowledged villains were worthy in the end, and sometimes even the good people of conscience were mistaken and misled. In fact, some of the Comstock's most admirable citizens were scamps when their wills were read; and it was clear that the good were as afraid to die as the bad.

Time was definite and clear and certain: the earth turned in its course, the sun rose and fell, and one season led to another. There was inevitable order in time. Yet even here, as in the rules for human beings, there were contradictions. She had lost her children when they should have lost her. She buried a son killed in the mines and another who returned from the war in France wounded, and she even buried a daughter who was strong and sound from the start, but died gracefully of old age.

Perhaps the confusing rules that were given to Grandmother's contemporaries had no meaning for her; perhaps with everyone it had been caprice. As she grew very old, Grandmother must have searched for some meaning for her own existence, and even now she must sometimes wonder about it; indeed, she must be amused that she who rather disliked pioneers should become the oldest of them.

Grandmother is probably amused as well by the coincidence of her life and the history of Virginia City, so alike in the vigor of their years. She must look back upon herself and the city with the detachment of the third person, for it is obvious now that the heavens have betrayed their pledge to let her see a century from the beginning to the end; and Grandmother can easily realize that, having seen it, she can do nothing about it.

Chapter Four

Chapter Four

MY GRANDMOTHER BELIEVES THERE IS A GOOD DEAL THAT CAN BE SAID FOR the Bible. She approves of it. Indeed, she approves of the Bible with the same enthusiasm as she approves of Emerson. It is good solid reading for the most part, and in places it is really fascinating. Perhaps it is more illogical than Emerson, but then the Bible moves with the same heroic tread. Grandmother particularly prefers the New Testament. It isn't as stubborn or miraculous as the Old, and it has a charming spontaneity that Grandmother finds agreeable.

When I was a boy she gave me a Bible for a present. That wasn't the real present, of course. The real one was a pair of all-leather boots, with the Bible included as a sort of subsidiary gift. I didn't want to read it, and Grandmother replied that she supposed it did look threatening. I really didn't have to read the Bible, she explained, if I didn't want to, for I probably wouldn't care for it now, but some day I might read the Bible.

"It does have your birth date between the Testaments, besides some other particulars, so you may as well keep it," she said.

Grandmother, though, had been forced to read the Bible. In the convent she had had to answer questions about it and to memorize some of the wisdom. In those days she looked upon the Bible as punishment, for if she misbehaved she was given a passage to memorize. She became adept at quotations, but she regarded the Bible as a churlish book; and she was often bitter with it.

But Grandmother reads the Bible now, along with the newspaper, her Emerson, which is required reading, and her real favorite of all, Washington Irving. It is not because she is churchly that Grandmother reads the Bible. She has not been to church while I have known her, except for funerals and marriages, and lately she hasn't been bothering about funerals.

Grandmother believes in God, however. She has a quiet respect for Him, and I imagine it would be to His benefit to have a similar respect for her. They do get along well, but by leaving each other strictly alone. She doesn't ask Him for a thing any more since He disregarded her family to let her husband die; and as yet He hasn't demanded too much of her.

Grandmother realizes no reason why she should fear Him, for if He is All and Everywhere, He hasn't been especially interested in her. She doesn't believe

He utilizes thunderbolts for His purposes, and she is sure that Hell is nonsense. He must fully understand that His Earth is trying enough without His making it any harder for people by casting them into an uncomfortable Hereafter.

The theories of Hereafters are familiar to Grandmother, for she has made something of a study of them. She thinks that the Indian's Hell is a much more interesting place than the white man's. The Hell that the Piutes fear is managed by an evil Indian named Avea-Dagii. It is his business to keep the sinful wandering painfully through a scorching desert, where the herbs are tainted and the springs have dead prairie dogs in them. Whenever the wanderers attempt to climb to the good land, Avea-Dagii frustrates them with a burning torch. The good land is in the care of Pah-Ah, who sees to it that there are plenty of stout squaws on hand, and more than enough of clear water and game, kept abundant through the seasons for brave Indians.

Such a Heaven and such a Hell please Grandmother for they are naïve and of a simplicity that fits into the fundamental pattern of life, the turn of the seasons and night and day. The names of the keepers, too, have a charming metrical beat. There is nothing so brusque as Hell and Devil.

As for Hell itself—well, it is involved and intricate.

It offers too many complications for Grandmother.

Yet she believes that a threat or two from the high places is as prudent for the white as it is for the red people. A thunderbolt or a high wind, or any grumbling in the heavens, is satisfactory enough. But never a threat of Hell. That's carrying things too far.

"I dread to think," she said, "what would happen if most people were not afraid occasionally. But Hell should be left out of it. Parents especially should be careful not to threaten their children with such a phenomenon. It's too much like frightening them with the Policeman."

Grandmother would attend church if the sermons varied; but most sermons, she has learned, are intended to be inspirational, and Grandmother doesn't want inspirations of that kind, for they are so depressing afterward. Besides, while she would enjoy being a better woman, she can tell by glancing around that she is pretty good as she is.

From the descriptions she has been given of Heaven, Grandmother would rather live in Virginia City, in her own home. Heaven would be too intangible for Grandmother. Of course, it would be a clean place; there's that much to be said for it. Otherwise, she wouldn't stay there a minute. It would also have to be firm and substantial and not given to trying to surprise a sensible woman with airy miracles.

She is inclined to doubt that in Heaven the people would be cared for by God, personally; but if He does attend to things Himself, then He should be reasonable with her. Whether or not she does get His personal attention, she is convinced that He will be fair. There really isn't any reason why He should not. For one, she has certainly been fair with Him.

Naturally, she hasn't believed everything His disciples have said. She has provoked them sometimes, when she did what she thought was right. God, though, will understand that His disciples are men and don't understand a woman. What she has done, at any rate, has been logical; and she did it on her own initiative. No one had to bully her into doing what she thought was right, for she was never a bit influenced by the threats the preachers credited to Him. Perhaps the threats were not His, or they may well have been intended for people who needed scaring and have come to her by mistake through shortsighted disciples.

Grandmother has never taken advantage of God, and she would not be surprised to be told officially that His disciples have. While she has a respect for those fervent, churchly people, and a sympathy for them, too, for they are sincere, she is sometimes irritated by ambitious believers who use God to better their business. They are taking advantage of Him to draw attention to themselves, which is shallow of them. That disturbs Grandmother. She feels that God, if He is Up There, as people say, isn't looking out for Himself down here. Either that, or He is entirely too easygoing for His own good.

For some time Grandmother has been faintly amused, but mostly irritated, by a woman who was a motion picture actress a decade ago and now writes self-conscious essays concerning her Saviour. I have kept Grandmother informed of the person's activities, even to sending her books to Nevada. Grandmother reads them with distaste, but also with a certain fascination. When a friend of ours died who had been a newspaperman, the essayist and one-time actress was asked for a statement. She replied that she regarded the man's death as simply another assignment, but his best one of all, of course.

It caused Grandmother to wonder what the newspapers were coming to. She pointed out that the man was dead, he was buried, and there was no getting around that.

I fear, though, that Grandmother owes something to this motion picture person. She has given her a point of conscientious indignation. Grandmother must pretend the task of defending Heaven against people she imagines God would find difficult to put up with. When the retired actress, for example, became a producer of motion pictures, she intended publicity for the event by starting the cameras of her company's first photoplay with a sunbeam a considerate scientist from Mt. Wilson had captured and harnessed for her. The sunbeam was to be converted into energy through a photostatic cell which would form a current automatically when the sun crossed the meridian.

Grandmother regarded this as just so much more loud nonsense from Hollywood, and the audacity of science, using such power for so small a task, made her pleasantly indignant. That the press regarded the affair as impressive, and that the newsreel men and people of importance were on hand in the lady's studio the morning the sunbeam was to be put to work, was just further evidence of foolishness, Grandmother could see.

She wrote, in a letter that bristled with exclamation points, that she would have enjoyed indeed being present when the actress and people of importance awaited the coming of the miracle.

"You see," she said, "the sun didn't cross the meridian that day! At least, no one saw it make the crossing because the skies blacked with rage and rain fell, and the heavenly defense for the little sunbeam was perfect.

"The incident should be taken as a lesson from the high places. It is a threat! I must say it is the only threat that has my complete approval. It is evident that the sun did not care to be in motion pictures!"

It was, in all, a triumphant day for Grandmother, for she has never liked motion pictures, either. She has refused even to be photographed. A photograph to her has neither dimension nor meaning, and she regards it as at once conceited and sentimental. People insist upon putting pictures in frames and hanging them on the wall, an act which Grandmother believes is simply to draw attention to their conceit and sentimentality. Besides, a photograph on the wall is depressing; and it becomes particularly depressing when it has been on the wall a long time.

Grandmother believes that sentimentality is the matter with motion pictures. She has no dislike for sentiment itself; her dislike is for sentimentality. Sentiment is the proper amount of emotion for an occasion while sentimentality is too much emotion. But there are not many people whose taste is reliable enough to experiment objectively with emotion. And that is the matter with motion pictures. They do try to revive one's memories and stir the emotions. Such effort is vulgar. She wants her emotions to come without promptings, if they must come at all; to come cleanly and clearly from her own feelings.

While Grandmother disapproves of stimulants for

the emotion, she contradicts herself by being tolerant of intoxicating liquors, especially of very good liquor. She objects instead to the people who drink it. She believes it should not be prohibited, as she is determined against most restrictions. As a young lady she had not been allowed to mention whiskey. The word had evil in it, and just saying it let evil into the mind, where it caused considerable havoc. Whiskey could be called "spirits," but "Demon Rum" was preferable. For Grandmother that was making too much of the matter, taking advantage of a beverage by disparaging it as a demon, instead of recognizing that the fault was with the drinkers.

She is not sure that for some people it might not be good occasionally to drink a bit and make spectacles of themselves. Drinking is one of the escapes for oppressed people, and for some of them it is the only escape except suicide; and it is less messy. For herself, she has found the world to be a pretty difficult place. Only through discipline has she been able to suffer it. She is proud enough to know that everyone cannot keep in command of himself as she has done. She wouldn't respect this sort of slipshod person, of course. She would pity him and keep out of his way.

Grandmother does not often drink, but when she does, it is with a good deal of rite. It has to be whiskey, to begin with; and only the very best whiskey. There are no such things as a cocktail or a highball; and sherry is not liquor, of course. There is only whiskey, and it may be served in two ways, straight or with warm water, which is the Irish manner. As for gin, I am sure Grandmother never heard of it.

The whiskey is kept in a locker, which is beneath the cupboard. The locker is referred to upon the proper occasion; for example, a marriage, or a divorce, or perhaps the arrival of a friend who has been a long time in some God-forsaken place like California. No one would suggest getting the whiskey except Grandmother. If there was to be whiskey, she would first get the glasses and put them face down on the sideboard. Then she would get the whiskey, turn the glasses face up again and fill them. One drink was all anyone was offered—or all anyone got, for that matter—because Grandmother, thinking one would want no more than a glass, would remove the whiskey and turn the talk to other matters.

Whiskey, as a rule, was not so neatly disposed of in Virginia City. Indeed, whiskey did act like the Demon or Devil, and he fought all the way through the working of the Comstock Lode, being alternately denounced and applauded, depending upon the quarters into which at the moment he was being received. Old Comstock himself was, as the equally old citizens did admit, a fearful drinking man, but he saved his soul by repenting frequently and enthusiastically in religion.

In the early days of the sixties when the town was beginning, he had insisted that the citizens patronize the church and demanded that the ministers give every dead man a lengthy and elaborate funeral. Sometimes, particularly if the dead man had been a bandit and expired suddenly, the ministers would find it indeed a problem to offer praises. But Comstock was firm about it. "Give him a good send-off," he insisted, "the best you got." The ministers were assured of plenty of payment.

Funerals became elegant in Nevada, and prospectors found it very pleasant while they were in town to attend all the funerals they could. It was easy to find funerals, for in those early days there was at least one a day, most of the citizens being impulsive. The funerals swept down B Street, where all the best livery stables were, on their way to the cemetery; and as they passed, they attracted the attention of idlers and patrons of the saloons, who joined the procession, unshaved and booted as they were, to be present at the ceremony and thus to learn who had died.

After some disagreeable precedents, the clergy never held a funeral at train time, for the mourners had to run to the depot to see who was arriving by railroad. Grandmother was told of the scandalous incident at the funeral of a gentleman named Sugar-Foot Jack, whose pallbearers abandoned his casket in the street when the train sounded its whistle.

The church, Grandmother said, got off to a bad start in Nevada. The first Catholic church was blown down by the wind and unpaid carpenters tore down and carted away the second Catholic church in Virginia City.

By the seventies, though, the citizens were ready for religion; in time, churches became the best buildings in town, built of brick and stone, and as able to combat the seasons as saloons. The people, being vigorous about everything, attended church with enthusiasm. Sunday broke the rhythm of the week, as everyone set aside a day to be good. Saloons were strictly forbidden to open until after the evening services, and even then the customers were given to quiet, thoughtful drinking.

For the most part denominations made little difference. The city was not old enough to have formed traditions or to have a fashionable religion. There was brisk competition between churches, but it had nothing to do with religion; the Baptists would try to have a better baseball team than the Methodists, or the Lutherans were determined that no other church would have more popular picnics. That was the rivalry, and if there was ever antagonism it was because the

Methodists had won a game or the Presbyterians held an extraordinary picnic. Religion itself was no problem; as everyone said of the sects, they all led to the same Place.

Chapter Five

Chapter Five

IN NEVADA IN THE SUMMER-TIME INDIANS CAME TO THE DOOR SELLING BASKETS OF pine nuts they had picked from the trees on the hillsides. Grandmother knew one of the Indians for many years. His name was Charley; Soldier Charley, the town called him because he wore an American army campaign hat, which was crusted with pine sap and streaked with service from the nights Soldier Charley had slept in stables. On occasion he also wore many medals, despite certain efforts from the army post, where there had been attempts to persuade him that his decorations meant nothing. Charley could not be convinced because he refused to speak English. He could speak it if he tried hard, but he was reluctant to try at all, for when he was persuaded to speak English he was invariably cheated of the proper price for his pine nuts.

Charley could do better with gestures. He would knock impatiently on the door, and keep knocking, too, until he was answered; and by then he was indignant. He would stand there belligerently, leaning back on his heels with his soldier hat pulled far down on his forehead, but not far enough to keep his fierce black hair out of his eyes. The basket of pine nuts he had selected for Grandmother to purchase was already placed on the doorstep. "Two bits," he would say, and repeat himself over and over again until he got his fee. Having completed the sale and put the money in the top of his shoe, he would salute, with his hand rigidly at his forehead. When he was younger Charley held the salute until it was answered, but some people didn't understand and failed to return it. He simply saluted now, and walked away, leaving the gate wide open behind him.

Grandmother sometimes talked to Charley, both of them using gestures. She would be smiling to let him see she was his friend, but Charley never indicated his pleasure. He just gestured and grunted. Grandmother would enquire of his family by pointing the height of his children, beginning below her knees and, with abrupt stops, raising her hand to her shoulders.

"How many, Charley?" she would ask, holding up a speculative three fingers.

Charley would shake his head and with his mouth make contemptuous noises. Grandmother would hold out four fingers, and Charley would nod.

Grandmother would enquire if he found the winter severe, indicating with a sweep of her hand the snow-covered mountains in the distance. Charley would shrug.

"Not bad. Horse die, squaw hungry. Not bad." And then wearied with all this chatter, Charley would salute again and move on.

After a difficult morning with housewives, Soldier Charley found it pleasant to select the Divide for his rest in the afternoon. He was likely to be very happy from all the fine whiskey he had drunk in the city and he would find his way to the Divide, indeed to the back of one of our sheds, where in the afternoon he could be seen sleeping sweetly. By evening Charley would be awake and wonderfully refreshed, for as he walked past the house Grandmother could hear him mumbling what abuse he was going to give his squaw.

Charley and his squaw had a place of their own in a shallow mine shaft. They were forbidden to live with the other Piutes because a great shame had come to Charley when he was a brave and wore a feather. The Piutes banded together in three camps, and in each of them much poker was played. One of the camps was in the Ravine, below the Divide, on the outskirts of the city, where the wigwams spread out like a patchwork quilt on a slope near a slender stream of water that leaked from the Water Works reservoir. The scrawny and unhappy-looking ponies were hobbled by the stream, to drink the water before it disappeared into the ground and to nibble the grass that grew there so hopefully in the desert.

The wigwams were of dirty cloth in many colors, patched with pieces of rusty tin, with a blanket covering the open side. The plumbing of the wigwams was an annoyance to the citizens in Virginia, for when the wind in a capricious moment decided to blow to the west, the windows in town had to be closed immediately and children summoned in from the streets. The wind must have been sympathetic, though, for it usually blew to the east.

The second Indian camp was below C Street, just above the railroad depot, but with a bluff between camp and city. Braves in overalls loitered by the depot, hoping that suddenly the train would arrive and a passenger request to take their picture and pay two bits for the privilege. Near the camp were most of the Piute washwomen. They did their washing very early in the morning, before even the sun was up, on rocks that had been smoothed and whitened by daily use for many years. By sunup the laundry was on the lines or draped on the rocks. The squaws would be sitting in fat little circles, playing poker. The game was all day long, until sundown, when the next day's washing arrived and the Piutes went to their wigwams.

The squaws caused competition in the clothes-washing business, for until they turned to it the Chinese had pretty much of a monopoly. The Chinese, though, brought most of the depression on themselves by a system they had of dampening the wash. They sprinkled water through their teeth, their mouths holding a pint of water at a time.

The Chinese were inclined to be bitter at their loss of business, especially since their squaw competitors washed within a hundred feet of Chinatown and seemed much nearer than that, indeed, on a day that the wind turned west. The Chinese, in time, left town, one by one.

Chinatown had been below the railroad depot, at the north end of the city, on the only really level ground in the Comstock district. The drainage of Virginia City ran directly through Chinatown and was utilized for irrigation of the vegetable gardens, and, some people said, for washing purposes. Chinatown was mostly wash-houses, each house with a raised floor and barrel tubs, the barrels being halved. The clothes were cleaned by slapping them against boards, by men almost always named John. Chinatown had one store, a large brick building of two stories that offered rice, hams and bacons, nuts, dried fruits, foreign candies, and prostitutes. Here the small boys from the city purchased their firecrackers for the Fourth of July. The Chinese themselves used the crackers to drive away the devils who gathered in the lowland. There were temples for the same purpose. These were called "joss houses," housing very ancient gods of wood and iron. The squaws, too, of a warm summer's day liked to sit in the cool temples and refer to the gods, but the Chinese discouraged the practice.

The third Indian camp was high on Mt. Davidson. The Piutes banded there somehow never felt at ease near the white men. For what money they needed they sold uprooted stumps to the city and marketed wild horses; they visited the city perhaps but once a year and then came as a delegation, with squaws and children, horses, dogs, and all. They usually stayed a week or so, paying formal call to the other camps and searching the city for garbage, which they stuffed into huge sacks and carried up the mountain. They were restless people, migrating around the mountain, following the two box flumes that carried the water to the city. Their horses were watered by leakage from the flumes and fed from the greenery that grew in the damp ground underneath. The Piutes were forced to follow the flumes because they supplied the only growth of the mountain except the sagebrush and mesquite and pine. But wherever the Indians moved about the mountain they still had flying over their heads a large American flag.

For the citizens, the flagpole was a fine place to

visit on a Sunday afternoon. At one time or another, everyone had eaten a picnic lunch there and carved his name on the flagpole, while he held his hat with one hand and squinted his eyes in the wind that swept over the mountain peak.

The city employed a man to walk up the mountain twice a day to raise and lower the flag at dawn and sunset. It was more than a five-mile climb and the flagman spent most of his day walking back and forth. "Why he never stays up there all day," Grandmother said, "has never been very clear to me."

The Piutes on the mountain maintained many of their tribal traditions, such as the dances of the seasons, but Virginia people were never encouraged to watch them. Grandmother questioned Soldier Charley about these rites on the hill, but he would not comment, although he disliked the mountain Piutes for they had brought the great shame into his life. They forced him to wear the clothing of a squaw. Skirts did not become Charley; besides, he resented his wife doing the hunting while he gathered wood with the giggling squaws. He had acquired an army hat and cigar medals and run away from the camp finally, but he always regarded himself as a failure. He had been made a squaw because he had not been brave in the last war against the white man.

The two major Indian wars in Nevada had happened before Grandmother arrived there. They were fought in 1860 and '61, and when she came to town in the spring of '62 the town was still ready to hold off the Indians who were expected any moment. Grandmother has heard many stories of the wars and of how savage the Piutes were, but from her own dealings with Indians she believes they must have been forced into the fighting. She knew that, before the war began, the chief, Winnemucca, had said that war with the white man would destroy all the tribes in Nevada, and it happened as he said.

A pony express messenger rode into Virginia City in the summer of 1860 to say that the Indians had burned Williams' Station, on his Carson River Route, and had murdered three men. The Comstock district. had already had trouble with the Indians. A trapper had shot and killed an Indian brave, not because he had stolen a trap, but because, the trapper explained, "he looked like he was going to." And the Indians had protested. Virginia City thought it was time to punish the Indians, and formed an army, arming each of the soldiers importantly with a rifle, a knife, and a pistol. But as an army they were a disorderly lot, and near Pyramid Lake a tribe of Piutes ambushed and massacred them. There was despair in Virginia City, but fortunately most of the men killed were not family men but prospectors. The despair was mostly caused by pride, since before the battle the Piutes had offered peace and the explanation that it was not their tribe that burned Williams' Station, but Shoshone Indians from Lake Tahoe, and that the burning had been done by two braves because the white men at the Station had captured their wives and would not release them. The two braves had gone to Winnemucca, since it was his territory, to demand revenge. The chief had refused, offering the gentle explanation that such outrages were sometimes expected from the white man. The braves said they would return to their tribe and get permission for revenge, but on their way back they had to pass Williams' Station and, being impulsive men, stopped in to rescue their squaws, kill the men, and burn the building.

Grandmother said that the explanation did not satisfy the Virginia City people, who had decided suddenly to shoulder the white man's burden. The citizens, chanting revenge, organized an army of seven hundred, many of them American soldiers. Winnemucca tried again to bring peace, traveling from tribe to tribe, requesting the Indians to retreat rather than fight. Himself, when all parleys failed, he began a seven-day fast and much impressed his contemporaries, but on the sixth day, when he must have been hungry indeed, the word came a white army was marching on Pyramid Lake. The Indians prepared for war. On the first attack the white army was trapped again and lost twelve of its cannon; in fact, all the cannon it had. The white army attacked the next day at dawn, though, to capture the Indian stronghold and commit another massacre. The Indians that survived fled. This was the last of the wars with the Indians, which the historians have called the Indian Uprisings.

Grandmother recalls that, although the wars were over, there was much excitement for the next year. Warnings came in weekly that the Piutes were organizing; that they were marching on the city; that, indeed, they were just beyond the nearest hill, holding a war dance. The city was very frightened and demanded soldiers from the government. A defense was erected on Devil's Gate, a high and narrow pass leading to the city. Boulders were carried to the top of the gate to be dropped on the heads of the Indians in case they should decide to march through the pass. In the excitement many families moved to California, and the women and children of the families remaining were requested to live in the courthouse, where school was held and a hospital was prepared. A soldier came to Grandmother, a week after her arrival, warning her to leave the hotel for the courthouse where, he said, "We won't let an Injun harm a hair on the head of the women-folk." Grandmother prom-

ised to run to the courthouse at the first ringing of the
fire bells or the first shot fired from the giant how-
itzer that had been anxiously placed on Devil's Gate.
But the Indians never came. Some of the city's most
admirable citizens, though, went out after them and
returned from brief skirmishes with scalps. The scalps
were carried to the city triumphantly and placed on
ramrods in the barrels of the rifles that had been hung
on the walls of saloons.

These early days of the Indian wars in Virginia
City were dominated by a man who became a legend,
H. T. P. Comstock. He was usually called Old Pan-
cake because he was such an impatient and ambitious
man that while he was prospecting he would not take
time from his work to bake bread. Instead, he would
prepare a pile of pancakes and eat them through the
day. He was appreciated by his colleagues for his facility with the frying pan. It is supposed to have been he
in the miners' anecdote who was able to pitch a pan-
cake from the pan through the chimney and run outside the cabin to catch the cake as it came down.

Comstock protested against the Indian fighting, not
because of his principles but because such disturbance
took his thoughts away from his work. His protest
was considered because he owned the largest diggings
in town and he controlled the sluice water. He com-
plained that he had a hard enough time keeping men

working without their going out to kill Indians. Comstock was eaten with ambition; he enjoyed thoroughly the respectful nods that were given him when he strode down the street, and he was delighted when his hirelings referred to him as the King of the Diggings. On his walks he would buy whiskey for those who spoke of the mines as the Comstock Lode.

Grandmother saw him once and described him as a tall and woebegone creature with an immense black mustache and clothes and boots that were too large for him.

"He always walked rapidly," she said, "and wore a worried expression, as though something had just gone wrong. He was a troubled man who always imagined that his destiny would make a martyr of him."

Comstock was one of the first men to be in Virginia City; indeed, he had been there while it was called Ophir City. Much of the mining property was in his name, and he had shrewdly secured almost all of the water rights. Since most of the work then was by rocker and sluice mining, Comstock was temporarily the dictator of the lode. He had three ambitions, and they seemed to weigh upon him. He wanted to have all the gold in the West; he wanted to marry beautiful women; and he wanted to go to Heaven the minute he died. Otherwise, as he often said, he didn't want to die at all. It looked, to begin with, as if Comstock would get his first ambition; in fact, he had enough gold to satisfy him almost; but he wasn't sure of his third ambition, and he had a great deal of trouble with his second.

He had purchased a wife from a Mormon named Carter, whom Grandmother described as a little, troubled man. He and his wife had come to Comstock's diggings on their way to Salt Lake, with all their belongings on a wagon drawn by tired horses. Comstock, since he needed laborers, suggested Carter stay awhile to rest before proceeding across the mountains; besides, he was attracted by Carter's wife. Grandmother heard gossip that Comstock was spending as much time as he could at Carter's wagon while Carter was in the mines. It seemed he liked to watch her combing her hair. Comstock finally left his diggings in charge of an assistant and ran away to Washoe Valley with Carter's wife. But the action seemed to worry him. He regarded it as near adultery. Therefore he took her to a preacher he knew and married her. The next day he brought his wife back to diggings and received congratulations. In the midst of the revelry, the first husband, Carter, appeared. He wanted his wife. Comstock, feeling outrated, swore he never saw such a mess. It was plain enough to him that if Mormons could marry more than one wife, then a

Mormon wife could marry another husband. But Carter intended to be stubborn, and Comstock finally had to buy Carter's interest in the lady. He gave him a horse, an unloaded pistol, and sixty dollars in silver. The first husband started out cheerfully enough, but Comstock called him back and demanded a bill of sale. Comstock pinned the receipt to his marriage certificate and put both of them in his wallet.

But in a week Comstock's wife ran away. He hired a posse and the sheriff too, and brought back his wife and a long-legged miner he had never seen before. He warned his wife, before witnesses, never to let it happen again. But with the spring she was gone, and he never heard of her again. Comstock again called in witnesses to declare that he was through with his wife. But that did not bring her back, either, and he took to the church with fervor. While he contended ever after that he would go to Heaven, Grandmother doubts that he ever did.

Grandmother doubts, too, that Comstock had as much to do with the Comstock Lode development as the city thought he had. She believes the discovery of the lode was made by two young Germans, the Grosch brothers, who came to Nevada when the territory was part of Utah and found a substance which they thought was silver. They employed Comstock to guard their claim while they returned to Sacramento to assay speci-

mens and negotiate a loan to develop their mine. On
their trip they were caught by the winter that swept
over the Sierras, and one of them died. The other continued and finally reached Placerville, after having
walked over a mountain range in the winter. But his
legs were frozen, and while he was resisting amputa-
tion he died. The papers of claim in his pocket were
dated 1851 and described the findings as "carbonate of
silver." Of course what he had found was a silver so
rich it was without precedent, and he was unable to
recognize it.

Grandmother said that nothing was done about the
Grosch claim, people being uncertain of what carbonate of silver could be, but that Comstock entered
claims for all the surrounding land, including the
water rights. He didn't develop his claims, but waited
until a number of men who had been prospecting
farther down in the valley struck a tough blue clay
that puzzled them, for it had a streak of gold in it and
gold had never been in clay before. They thought it
was a worthless metal which they called "quick gold."
They decided to mine it anyway, but Comstock denied
them the use of his water for their sluices unless they
gave him shares in the claim. This is the way, Grandmother said, that gold and silver were discovered in
Virginia City; and it was the way, too, that Comstock
gained control of it.

Comstock could have had his first ambition, to have all the gold; but he sold his shares to San Francisco mining companies because the ground was difficult to develop. He purchased shares from miners for fifty dollars or whiskey or a new revolver, and sold them to the mining companies for hundreds of dollars, imagining that his profit was tremendous. But when mining machinery was brought to the Comstock Lode, the profit of one mine in the first four years was fifteen million dollars. It was the Ophir mine, and Comstock had owned the ground. The aggregate of all mines in the first twelve years was more than $145,-000,000, the income being from $2,000,000 to $17,000,000 a year. In the seventies and eighties, the years Grandmother was raising her children, the income of the mines rose to $40,000,000 a year and often a good deal more. Grandmother said that toward the last of his life Comstock was a very bitter man.

The machinery for mining had to be brought over the mountains. It came first by prairie schooner and then later by railroad, a shipment of it in pieces requiring twenty or thirty flat cars. Its arrival in town was an event. Grandmother, along with her neighbors, would be down at the depot to see it arrive and watch a massive piece being dragged to the mines on rollers by a span of horses. The Indians came, too, and watched with amazement. The machinery in operation frightened them. It was part of the white man's magic, and they avoided it.

Grandmother had a Piute washerwoman who refused to turn on an electric light. Since the wash shed was quite dark even in daytime, she had to bring her son to work with her to turn on the light. He was a chubby little boy about six years of age, very shy and unable to speak English. He would turn on the light without hesitation and then start for home, followed by a dog he traveled around with who didn't understand English either.

Grandmother's washerwoman refused to touch the electric light because she feared it would destroy her. Grandmother could not dissuade her from it, for the first electric light the squaw had seen was in a grocery store near the Chollar mine. The squaw had been accustomed to arriving at the store very early in the morning to get scraps of food, and one day when she went to the store, the store was gone. The ground underneath it had collapsed and the store, groceries and grocer, had fallen hundreds of feet into an abandoned mine shaft. The only evidence left of the grocery was an electric wire, hanging from a telephone pole, and spluttering. The squaw knew immediately what had happened. It was more of the magic.

Chapter Six

Chapter Six

ONCE A WEEK, ON EVERY SATURDAY MORNING, MY GRANDMOTHER RE-turns to her room to oil and polish her revolver. Grandmother regards it as a chore, and a disagreeable one at that; but she has been keeping the revolver oiled and polished for fifty years now; indeed, ever since her husband died, leaving her his family and revolver to provide and care for. Grandmother goes to her task bravely, with firmness in her face, and always leaves behind her the warning that while at her task she does not wish to be disturbed by anyone. There could, however, be scarcely a reason for disturbing Grandmother, for she has already completed the business of the morning, and in such a brisk manner that the household realizes that now the time has come to oil and polish the revolver.

The weapon is kept in Grandmother's bureau drawer, under some lace handkerchiefs. It is a very large black gun, wonderfully sinister, being a thirty-eight caliber Colt on a forty-five police stock, that holds five copper shells as fat as thumbs. The weapon, of course, is much too heavy for Grandmother to shoot, and if ever she shot with it she would be sure to break a wrist, if not an arm. But she keeps it polished anyway, all the while regarding it with thin distaste. It is to her the black sheep of the family. I don't know precisely why she keeps it, for she knows very well that some night in the dark it is likely to be treacherous and go off by itself; but I suppose Grandmother regards it as a necessary precaution.

There is a reason, though, why Grandmother attends to the revolver every Saturday morning. Saturday nights in Virginia City had once been given an uproarious discord with good citizens defending themselves in a lively state of chaos. Grandmother knew that on Saturday night there was the Devil to Pay. Once a week on this night the miners had money, and some of it got to the renegade whites and to the Indians and they, in turn, invested it in whiskey—and very bad whiskey it was. It was necessary for the men who had families to remain at home, behind drawn curtains.

The Indians have been tame for some time and now, trying to live in a white man's world, they have become pathetic; but sixty and seventy years ago, in the sixties and seventies, they were still sensitive of the outrage against them and often, when encouraged by whiskey, felt a surge of sudden bravery.

Some of them believed they should impress the white man with their power; and the way they went about it was to promenade, which meant strutting and threatening with a pounding of breasts. A promenade, though, seldom progressed to a rampage, for that meant fighting in the hills with soldiers from the fort.

Grandmother's neighbors were sometimes shocked because she had sympathy for the Piutes' promenade. She didn't go very deeply into the matter; she just thought that the Indians' feelings had been hurt, and she believed that they would remain harmless enough if they were left alone during a promenade.

"The way to do it," she said, "is to ignore them. Let them strut and threaten, but pretend you don't even see them. Don't try to reason with them, for they think in different standards." "Never," she insisted, "let them feel you are afraid."

Sometimes on a promenade the Indians would knock on the door to insist upon coming into the house. Grandmother would ignore the knock. As a boy I was cautioned never to open the door for an Indian, except our old Piute washerwoman. But in the sixties and seventies the new settlers were confused and frightened by the demands of an Indian.

The Indian would be some dowdy brave with an odor and a bedraggled feather tied in his thick black hair. He would swagger through the doorway with a grunt, make his way to the cupboard, eat all he could, and carry off in his arm whatever provisions he found. If the housewife screamed or even timidly asked him to leave, he would threaten her with his knife, usually an old vegetable knife, but one that looked terrifying to a woman who had never before had an Indian in the room alone with her. He would make terrifying faces, too, grimacing and drawing his finger across his forehead. If she had her children with her he would often threaten them, one at a time, by placing his knife against their throats. On one of these kitchen promenades a boy who had seen his sister threatened got his father's rifle and killed the brave. That put a temporary stop to promenades.

Grandmother had a less forceful but equally effective method. She had learned early that an Indian was no more menacing than a child. While he liked to be self-consciously brave and to threaten, he could be likewise frightened with threats, provided one threatened to tell his squaw of his drinking. For the Piute squaws have always been notorious husband beaters.

Yet, now in Virginia City's comparatively peaceful days, Grandmother keeps her revolver for the same reason that her husband did; just in case the Piutes or renegades went on a rampage. Once a son attempted to substitute a small automatic for it, but Grandmother reminded him of what his father had said: that a gun was worthless that did not have a bullet large enough to knock down its victim, no matter where the victim was hit.

Somehow Grandmother has always pictured her potential assailant as a maniac, and she realizes that an automatic's bullet would go right through a maniac, but that in his frenzy he would keep right on coming. She would hit him with a forty-five, and he would be stopped for sure.

When I was seven and very inquisitive, I was curious about that gun. Sometimes, while Grandmother was away, I would steal into her bedroom to slide open the drawer noiselessly and look at the gun in all its sullen magnificence. In time I was taking it from the drawer and brandishing it before the mirror to see how well I looked with it.

It is discouraging to be a gunman at seven years of age, though. For once, while I had the revolver pointed at the mirror, I accidentally pulled back the hammer. The gun cocked with a click, and the noise of it was so ominous that it scared me. I couldn't release the hammer. I thought of tapping the hammer against the floor, but that might fire the shell, and the explosion would take place in Grandmother's bedroom, a very private place that I should not have been in, to begin with. I thought about the predicament for at least an hour, while the minutes went menacingly by. Finally, when I heard Grandmother returning, I returned the gun to the drawer, carefully covered it with handkerchiefs again, and tiptoed from the room to greet Grandmother self-consciously.

But conscience overcame me that night while I was praying to God to uncock Grandmother's revolver, and I awakened her to confess what I had done. Grandmother was alarmed. She sent me from the room while she put on her robe, and then she went straight to the drawer and lifted out the revolver with two fingers. She placed it in her straw hat and carried it out to the woodshed, where we both stood looking at it. We decided that before releasing the hammer we had better take the dog from the woodshed and put him in the yard. I was told to stand behind Grandmother. But when she picked up the gun and pointed it at the earth, she couldn't release the hammer either. We called the Piute boy and sent him to get Mr. Murphy from the Waterworks up the street. Mr. Murphy came trotting, in his sheepskin coat with his nightgown tucked into his trousers.

"Take this," said Grandmother, "and see what you can do."

Mr. Murphy looked at her and then he looked at me. He took the revolver from the straw hat and with a practiced motion of his thumb released the hammer. He put the gun into his pocket.

"Mrs. Flannery," he said, "what *were* you going to do?"

Grandmother told him she wasn't going to do anything with it, that she had simply attempted to release the hammer and had failed, and now she would like the gun back. But what use had she for such a powerful revolver, Mr. Murphy wanted to know.

"I keep it," Grandmother explained, "for protection."

Grandmother returned her revolver to its drawer, but without scolding me; and I never went near it again, although I often did want to see the engraving on its barrel of a stagecoach being robbed by masked men. Grandmother herself had told me of many coach hold-ups, and had even been in one. She enjoyed it thoroughly. One of the bandits had removed his black felt hat before requesting her to step from the coach.

"In Nevada," she wrote to her family in New England, who must have been startled, "it is not necessarily considered criminal to commit robbery. To waylay and apprehend a stagecoach is neither ethical nor unethical. It is simply a means of securing money; not much different, that I can see, from many other methods less exciting. There is a procedure, which is abrupt.

A coach, rounding a turn of the Grade, is confronted by a band of men on horseback and wearing masks. The driver halts his coach, with much dust raised, to surrender the Wells, Fargo money box. The driver surrenders the box without prompting from the bandits, as though he expected it all along and didn't mind a bit. You must remember that he is giving away money that belongs to people referred to vaguely as Eastern Interests. He knows no more of them than that.

"Some of the drivers, I should add for sake of the story, are accused of conspiring with the bandits, but I believe that is too complicated an arrangement.

"When Flannery and I arrived, bandits did not molest travelers. The express box was their ambition; the travelers were not worth the trouble. But the stage company began the unfortunate practice of disguising the money on employees who pretended to be passengers. The bandits, then, were forced to search everyone. That is a bad element, as you see, to creep into the ranks of stagecoach robbers, for travelers now are disturbed and even robbed. I assure you Virginia City is indignant."

It was discouraging to the future of all stage robbers to have a few rascals among them who bothered passengers, for in mining communities where everyone is known, including the highwaymen, a mask is not much of a disguise at the moment of robbery, and citizens could later protest. No one, naturally, would protest if Wells, Fargo was robbed, for they were probably just a pair of Eastern Interests.

In another letter, Grandmother recalled an apology the robbers offered after one outrage in which travelers had been troubled. The highwaymen in December of 1869 robbed a coach outside of Silver City and, because they were forced to ask the passengers to dismount, spread out coach robes for the ladies and gave the gentlemen champagne. The bottles were first offered to the ladies who, of course, had to decline; but the bottles were distributed generously among the gentlemen. Guests and robbers mingled together and toasted each other gallantly, there on the side of a hill outside Silver City, while the driver looked again and again at his heavy gold watch, complaining that his schedule was absolutely ruined.

Wells, Fargo finally thwarted robberies by hiring men from California, noted for their bravery, to ride in advance and in the rear of the stagecoaches. Shooting began then, where all before had been peaceful, and newspapers of the period were excited with the contests of marksmanship. The bandits were frustrated, yet in retaliation devised a new form of robbery. It began on the morning of November 1, 1870, when Nevada's favorite outlaw Jack Davis with his band held up and robbed the Overland Express, an act which was regarded as the first train robbery in the world. The Nevada newspapers praised Nevada for its daring outlaws.

Grandmother had seen Jack Davis. Her husband pointed him out on the street. He was a small, quiet man, whom the *Enterprise* described as the "Professor." He was given to gambling, and when he had money he was welcomed into the very best poker games, the games in the Crystal Saloon that included judges and government attachés. He was very popular and could always be counted among those who would donate to charity. But he became too ambitious, and one evening stole a train and hid it in a tunnel. The tunnel was on a spur of the railroad line and was a quiet place where the robbers could work without interruption. They got fifty thousand dollars in gold.

The government wouldn't stand for that. Jack Davis and his group were sent to prison, and his enterprises ended. He had been operating the mill in lower Gold Hill where the money he stole was melted into bars of bullion and sold back to the government at a reasonable figure. Employees of the mill had received regular mill-rates, five dollars a day.

But other bandits were not as well liked as Jack Davis and his men, and because of them Grandfather

had to carry his revolver, especially when he was returning home in the evening, for this was the time
when footpads were at work. The footpads preferred
to rob on the Divide, near Grandmother's house, for
the Divide was between Gold Hill and Virginia and
many citizens walked from one place to the other. It
was darker on the Divide, too, and there were abandoned mine shafts convenient to pitch the victims in.
The footpads usually killed their victims and robbed
them afterward. By throwing them into an old mine
shaft, the murder would not be discovered immediately and the footpads were able to continue robbing
in the same place the remainder of the evening. Just
robbing the victim would have brought the police,
and that would naturally have meant complications
and discomfort; murder made it easier. Besides, there
was a good chance that the victim recognized his robbers and, if he lived, would identify them to the police. It was wise for a citizen to carry a revolver while
he crossed the Divide. Grandfather carried his in his
hand.

Footpads were considered the lowest of the criminals. Highwaymen and "saloon chiefs" were treated
with some respect, but the capture of a footpad meant
a hanging before morning. And saloon chiefs joined
the citizens' vigilante committee. Saloon chiefs were
the acknowledged Bad Men, and they were quite

proud of it. Each chief ruled a saloon. It was his head-
quarters. He plotted his dirty work there, whether the
dirty work was to be the death of a politician or the
humiliation of another saloon chief. Saloon chiefs
were expert gunmen, accomplished in all forms of
fast pistol-drawing and dagger work in close-quarters
cutting. A man's facility could be judged from his
saloon, for saloon chiefs graduated to better stations
as they improved their style. The town tolerated them
because they never molested miners. Before a shooting between the chiefs, the miners were urged to step
out to the safety of the street. If they decided to stay,
of course, it was at their own risk.

Grandmother remembers many of the notorious
chiefs, such swaggermen as Henry Robbins, Sandy
Bill Collier, and Sugar-Foot Jack. They all came to
sudden ends. One of her favorite stories, because it
has something of a moral, concerns a character known
as Farmer Peel. She is likewise very fond of his name.
He was such an unreasonable villain, was Farmer
Peel, that he even refused to pay his police fines; and
all the officers were reluctant to remind him. Most of
the chiefs were rather obliging about fines. They paid
cheerfully enough, as a sort of bounty for murdering
an enemy. In fact, Sugar-Foot Jack, who was the
smoothest of them, reported to court immediately
after he had killed his man, a desperado named Rob-

inson, to confess the deed without having to be prompted. Naturally, he testified that Robinson had drawn his pistol first, and that he had killed him not only in self-defense but because he was not certain Robinson was such a good shot he would miss a miner who was standing by, having a drink of beer. Sugar-Foot paid his fine and received the congratulations of the court.

But Farmer Peel defied the court and killed the deputy who served his summons. After that, he dared the law to come and get him, adding that he could be found any time in the Ophir Saloon. This was going too far, some people said; other citizens, though, regarded Farmer Peel as the stanchest of his contemporaries.

Farmer Peel's challenge became a public issue. Meetings were held in other saloons than the Ophir in which the citizens decided to support him against the group who were determined to take steps. Finally, on the trial morning, the Judge himself apprehended Farmer Peel at the bar in the Ophir Saloon.

"Come to court, Peel," he said. "The State wants the likes of you."

The Judge, whose name was Davenport, was a small, thin man with a long white beard; Farmer Peel pretended fear. He followed willingly enough to court and leaned against the rail to smile at his friends while the bailiff proclaimed the session. The town was surprised and crowded into the courthouse. What had happened, they wanted to know, that made the Farmer come to court? He'd swing for his killing. Murmurs of excitement ran over the spectators.

The Judge demanded order, and got it, and very gently enquired if the defendant had counsel. What was that, Peel wanted to know; and when he was told, he said that he did not need any lawyer to settle his troubles.

"I'll do my own work here," he said, confidently, and with a great laugh he leaned over the bench and pulled Judge Davenport's long, white beard.

Some of the spectators laughed, but most of them kept their eyes away as Farmer Peel strode from the courtroom, his black coat open and his hand on the handle of his gun. Then something happened that caused great fear and finally became a fable. As Farmer Peel was unwinding the reins from the hitching rail, while the Judge was in the courthouse crying, he must have frightened his horse, for the horse reared and kicked Farmer Peel in the head and killed him.

Everyone in town was very impressed. It was wonderful, and it was awful. It was a deliberate act of God, and men talked of it anxiously for weeks, hushing in alarm when the minister strolled triumphantly

down the street, as proud as if he had personally ne-
gotiated it.

The saloon chiefs, however, continued to rule Nevada street life until late in the eighties; until, in fact,
the death of Fighting Sam Brown, who was as feared
a man as Farmer Peel. Sam Brown, too, was asked to
come to court, following a series of murders. He refused, stating he was indignant. But the prosecuting
attorney was likewise indignant. He went from one
saloon to another, at each one declaring that he had
challenged Fighting Sam to meet him in court, and
that Brown had been too cowardly to come. The chief
came the next day; indeed, he waited impatiently for
court to open, and then came striding in, his spurs
dragging angrily across the floor. He was met by the
attorney, who held a derringer in his hand. Sam
Brown, thus disarmed, was fined five hundred dollars.
Such humiliation infuriated him, and to justify himself he took a revolver from the first man he met and
then shot the man, who was a servant of a farmer
named Van Sickle. When the word came to Van Sickle
that one of his workers had been molested by a saloon
chief, he mounted his horse and, shotgun in hand, began a search for Sam Brown. He found him and finally
rode up to within reaching distance of the astonished
saloon chief, pointed his shotgun carefully, and blew
him to pieces.

The incident so pleased the citizens of Virginia City that they offered to elect Van Sickle to Congress, or any other office that he wanted. But he refused and went back to his farm. He also refused to lead a vigilante group that was forming. Grandmother approved of him thoroughly. Grandmother could approve, that is, from a distance. Aloof from the violence, she approved in theory. But it was embarrassing to her that her husband's family, the Flannerys, were known as "terrible fighters." They were large-limbed and strong, and had the tempers it took for mining and fighting. Her husband, as the eldest of the brothers, was the least impulsive, although he had sometimes cautioned his associates that he had what he called an uncontrollable temper.

Grandfather was the first of the family in Virginia City, having been sent there by San Francisco mining men as a representative of the California office. In time, he was put in a position to hire men; of course, he hired his brothers first. "Come," he said, "to the Big Bonanza."

Grandfather wanted men working with him whom he could trust. Westerners could be trusted, but only to a certain point. Easterners could likewise, but he knew that point in Easterners. The West had a civilization of its own, and, with it, ethics and morals of its

own. It was a new world that did not share the standards of the old, and it confused Grandfather. For one
thing, it was an affront to society for him to turn
down a request for a loan. If he could not negotiate
the loan, he was supposed to find some one who could,
and to do it simply because he had been asked in the
first place. At the same time it was considered all right
for him to swindle a friend if his friend had money;
but if he was without money, Grandfather must get
him some. Grandfather was supposed to recognize
everybody as his friend and equal, although he might
know one to be a scamp. He was, of course, permitted
the pleasure of calling the man a scamp while he was
elsewhere. However, after the scamp had been disparaged by everyone present, some one would surely
say, in a much different tone, "but he's a good-
natured felly, anyway." Then Grandfather and all
present were supposed to agree. But Grandfather
wouldn't do that. He was likewise expected to greet
the scamp as his friend when he met him, and Grandfather would not do that, either. Grandfather had to
become a reasonably good fighter.

He was glad in these hectic times to have his
brothers with him. The city's silver was greatly influ-
encing New York and dominating San Francisco. The
stock boards in both cities indicated silver stock rising

and falling swiftly, and investors wanted to know the reasons. Mine owners, though, permitted no visitors in sections of drifts that were being developed.

Except for some of the surface gold, most gold and silver appeared in quartz, a hard mineral often exquisite with crystals. The Comstock Lode, a huge quartz ledge, long and wide as a valley river, ran the length of Virginia City, directly underneath the town, and on to Gold Hill and Silver City, in varying depths beneath the surface, from a few feet to five miles in the earth.

A company that struck quartz was worth developing, for it was almost certain to strike gold or silver and sometimes both; but a mine that missed quartz was not, at that time, worth developing further. Mines that missed the quartz ledge were "wild cats." They struck *borrasca*, bad luck. Mines in quartz were digging in *bonanza*, good luck. It was difficult for an investor or speculator to tell whether the mine had struck borrasca, or bonanza down below. And to know was so important.

Silver veins were measured in rods, not feet, and were without precedent. A vein eight rods wide was eight times sixteen feet, which was enough silver to keep speculators in a state of extreme agitation. An investment in a stream of silver eight rods wide meant a fortune for the speculator himself and for generations to come of his family. He could make a million dollars in a fortnight; sometimes, by a clever manipulation of stock, in an hour.

Brokers and speculators tried desperately to secure information from the miners. Bribing miners was not too difficult, but miners were usually misinformed. A crew might be working in a silver vein with the miners ignorant of the ledge they were picking. Pick men were kept picking, and not even shovers could stop to examine their ore. Neither were the men allowed to work from one place to another in the mine. A man placed in a level three thousand feet below the surface could not descend to the four-thousand-foot level.

Each mine, however, had a crew of men that could be trusted; that is, trusted to a reasonable point. This was the crew assigned to develop new drifts and to bring specimens to the surface for assaying. They were well paid, the members of this crew, and they were expected, in return, to camouflage the value of the mine.

If the salary of an ordinary miner was five dollars a day, the salary of a trusted miner was fifteen, with a bonus for rapid work and a closed mouth. Grandfather selected and managed these crews for one mine, and he gave them, to begin with, one rule. They must not tell their wives of their work. But of course

Grandfather told Grandmother a lot more than he intended.

These trusted miners must have often been tempted. Speculators offered them commissions of cash, new hats, and stone houses. The men admitted to making the most of it, but by misinforming the speculators. If the information slipped out of a real vein that had been discovered, then every one of the crew was discharged. No one was employed again, either, until the informer had been caught. It was the discharged crew's concern to discover the informer in their midst. Found, he was persuaded to leave town.

Grandfather drafted his brothers to help him select the crews. The brothers had to maintain a dignity and obviously be men of repute. For one thing, they decided not to drink; or, if they did drink, not to show it.

The youngest of Grandfather's brothers was Patrick; he was too young for his job. Grandfather regretted that he had brought him to Virginia City, thus assuming a responsibility that was not exactly his, for Patrick had run away from school to follow his older brothers. Grandfather was forced to hire him, too. He was scarcely twenty, but he had been born late in his parents' lives and he matured early. He was strong, perhaps stronger than any of his brothers; but where the others were steadfast, he was plastic. He greeted the West breathlessly; at once he decided to be a Westerner. His speech became colloquial, he parted his hair in the middle, and he grew a fierce black mustache that bristled like a bandit's. His boots were high and elaborately carved, and his belt, for which he surrendered his suspenders, was the blackest and widest he could buy in all of San Francisco. His dress became self-consciously careless. The legs of his corduroy trousers were stuffed into his boot tops with wonderful untidiness; he hooked his thumbs into his magnificent black belt; and his stride was slow and wide and heavy. He even began to let his shoulders droop as though the years of prospecting were weighty upon him.

When Patrick came to Virginia City he was exactly Grandmother's age; but his sister-in-law, being married and already having a child, must have seemed older to him. At any rate, he gloried in being an uncle. Uncle Patrick, he wanted to be called. His brothers to him had all been fathers, and stern ones, too, who could be advisers but not confiders. In Virginia City, though he lived with his brothers in the town's one hotel that didn't have small animals of one sort or another, he came often to Grandmother's home—for the meals, he said; but it was mostly to talk.

Patrick would come early, direct from work, to cut

wood or run errands, or to lend books and magazines which would later give him the opportunity to come after them. When supper was over, he helped with the dishes while Grandfather with great preparation outlined work for the next day at the mine. Grandmother had to invite Patrick often because the evenings that she did not he gave to gambling and drinking, two recreations he took to with enthusiasm. His brothers could not curb him. He was as strong as they, and he couldn't be punished physically. Reprimands after each night out left him promising to be a better boy. He would swear it in a phrase that came easily to him, "by all that is Holy to me." And the next night he would be drunk again, to be the next day repenting his sins lengthily to Grandmother.

Grandmother did not protest when Patrick's brothers suggested with force that he should marry and settle down, as they phrased it. He was sent to San Francisco and instructed to return with a wife they had selected; but his adventures in San Francisco made Market Street history. He had money, vitality, and an infinite capacity for whiskey. He had to be summoned home.

Yet Patrick did find a wife; indeed, he found her in Virginia City. He married her of a moment, and he did not bring her to meet Grandmother. She was described as a "sporting woman." But Grandmother said that was nonsense. She was, said Grandmother, a foolish and a very young thing who tried to live up to her reputation. Grandmother on an afternoon after the marriage had gone to the city to call upon her. Grandmother described her as a pretty creature, dressed beyond the height of fashion. She called herself an actress, but it was whispered she was a dancer and, therefore, no good. Grandmother suggested that she and Patrick move to the Divide and live in one of Grandfather's houses. But the bride said that would place her among housewives, and she just hated housewives: they gossiped and pried so. She would prefer to stay in the hotel. Besides, she disliked housework, especially cooking. Grandmother invited her for tea, but she never came, of course.

After a week Patrick and his wife separated. She had left him, he said. He quit his work and, in need of advice, came to Grandmother, who suggested that he send his wife to her home and settle some money on her, for divorces then were cause for alarm. Patrick's wife, though, refused to return home, and declared she intended to remain in Virginia City as if nothing had happened. Patrick thought this was very embarrassing, but it was quickly over.

For that night, when Patrick was walking down C Street, a man made a remark about his wife. Patrick, upholding the code of a gallantry he scarcely understood, challenged the man. He intended to fight with his fists, but, as he attacked, his opponent stabbed him in the stomach and with both hands pulled up the blade to Patrick's chest. He tried to retrieve the knife, but it was wet and it fell to the sidewalk, and the man ran to leave Patrick staggering in the street, trying to hold in his intestines. Almost blindly and with all his strength, Patrick ran the two miles between Virginia City and the Divide, stumbling but still holding in his stomach, until he reached the hill that led to Grandmother.

It was late at night, but Grandfather was still at the mines. When he heard of the stabbing, he borrowed a horse to ride breathlessly home. But Patrick had died, in the chair by the range in the kitchen, before the doctor could arrive. He was in pain but he didn't feel it entirely, for he was preoccupied with the fear of dying and the fact that his big black belt was bloody.

Grandfather didn't hesitate long over the body; he murmured a prayer and crossed himself, and went to the bedroom to get his revolver.

"Who did it?" he asked. He put the gun in his pocket under his coat.

"Poor boy!" she said. "I do not know. He was gone too quick for that."

Grandmother had answered very quickly, and before she could be questioned again, she covered her face and ran from the kitchen to send the Piute boy for the priest.

She even told the sheriff that Patrick passed away before he could name his murderer. Yet she knew, of course. Patrick had told her. Not until later, when her husband and the murderer both were several years buried, did Grandmother mention the story. Somehow, though, the murderer seemed to know that Patrick had told, for he avoided Grandmother; and once, when she came face to face with him in a theatre lobby, he bowed and left.

Grandmother never named him because in those days justice was still a matter of personal revenge. Citizens did not depend upon the police, for the police were few and most of them were trustless. Grandmother does not approve of policemen, anyway. She dislikes them as much as she does the soldiers who came in times of labor troubles. Their coming inevitably meant murders, for striking miners would fight back hard.

Grandmother was disturbed when in the eighteen-seventies there was so much crime that citizens banded into a vigilante group to call themselves the "601." They hanged killers and gave known criminals "tickets of leave," which were warnings to leave town. The vigilantes' work was silent and swift, and for a while it kept the town free from bad men. Grandmother was glad when it disbanded, though, for the "601" intended to enter politics and give the state representatives of its choice. And she did not believe that such an organization would be competent to select public representatives. It was too sinister and theatrical for Grandmother.

Policemen, like soldiers, are too militaristic for her. It had been the custom of Virginia City to hire policemen from other places. The citizens who knew each other so well disliked or feared to govern their neighbors; besides, they were trained to be miners or storekeepers, not constables. It was simpler to hire men who had been stagecoach guards or soldiers or policemen in other cities. Grandmother tried to tell her husband that this was a mistake. Policemen should be from one's home town and know the people, she explained; then they won't be suspicious of the citizens, but will protect them instead. But her husband said that such a plan would do for a little town. Virginia City was the second largest city west of Chicago. Besides, he explained, Grandmother didn't understand such things; after all, she was a woman.

Chapter Seven

Chapter Seven

GRANDMOTHER HAS BEEN UNABLE TO APPROVE OF THE POLICE BECAUSE they pry so. While she refers to them as the authorities, they have never tried their authority on her; and if they ever did, there would be trouble. Oh, Grandmother might answer a question or two about her activities; but if she had been ordered to change an opinion, and faced the predicament of changing it or being arrested, Grandmother would surely go to jail. Indeed, if the law ever forced itself upon her, she would regard it as presumptuous and distinctly impudent, and she would have nothing whatever to do with it. The law could threaten or cajole—she would simply ignore it.

Grandmother has always upheld the rights of privacy, particularly independence of opinion and freedom of imagination. Like Voltaire, she may disagree with everything a person says, but she will defend to the death his right to say it.

Grandmother even defended her grandson's privacy, which was very helpful, for Heaven knows it is often exasperating to be both a philosopher and a cowboy at ten years of age. Cattle-tending on the deserted side porch demands readiness for sudden excitements and agitations, while philosophy at ten depends upon lofty contemplation and an attitude toward the world of weary authority; to be both philosopher and cowboy in the same morning is extremely difficult, for a man may tire after a moment of musing in the high place, and then he must return to the earth to get in the saddle, after an enemy Indian. Naturally, a man dislikes to be surprised in his concentration or astride the porch rail, digging spurs into an invisible animal. The first sight of such activities immediately interested the family, but Grandmother could walk past the porch and not even notice.

Grandmother was sometimes admonished for pampering her grandson. She did not discipline him enough, and he would certainly suffer for it later. It was easy for his uncles and his aunts and his cousins to see that, between the pampering of his grandmother and that of his mother, he was growing up to be a headstrong and petulant young man; and it was mostly his grandmother's fault, for she did not believe in punishment. For a boy there are inevitably many rules, but Grandmother tried to keep them at a minimum. He must not wear his new shoes every day, and in any shoes he must not kick open doors; he must wear a cap, but never in the house; he must not shred the newspapers to get at the comic page, and he must not read with his feet on another chair, even if it is the only comfortable way—all these rules, that seem to be forced upon him for no reason at all, prey upon a boy, and a spirit whispers to him to get out of the house for the tolerance of the sky.

With Grandmother, though, a boy could speak his opinions, if he didn't get excited and shout them. He could quietly argue out a point until he understood why, for example, he was not allowed to cut the bib from his overalls to make them look like a man's trousers, and he could upon occasion wear his cap backward if it made him feel like an automobile race driver. Grandmother never enquired what he had in his pockets that made them bulge so, and she never told him to take all the things out of his pockets right away and put them on the table. And when she hung up his clothes at night the privacy of his pockets remained unmolested. Grandmother let her grandson read as much as he pleased. She never enquired what he was reading, even though she had been warned over and over again that reading so much was not good for a young boy; he might get wrong ideas. The uncles and aunts and cousins had been wonderfully interested in whatever he was reading and peered over his shoulder without apology. They never seemed really satisfied unless they saw the book was either the *Sixth Arithmetic* or *The Motor Boat Boys*. Even Grandmother was cautioned about her reading, but for another reason : her eyes would suffer for it.

Most of the family's reading was done in the *Ladies' Home Journal*. The house seemed filled with the issues of it. Each bedroom had at least two copies; the sitting room had a fat little stack of them, and volumes of them were tied with string and stored away. The neighbors sometimes borrowed late issues or some of the old volumes. It is not likely that a copy of the *Journal* was ever thrown away.

Grandmother, though, seldom read the magazine; she had not subscribed to it, nor did she ever pay for it. To begin with, Grandfather had thought that his wife should know something about needlework, and he subscribed to *Godey's Lady's Book*. Somewhere in the seventies *Godey's* quit coming and another woman's magazine began. It continued coming for fifty years, with never an explanation. After a decade or two, Grandmother refused to write any more letters of cancellation to the editor.

There were a few magazines, however, that Grandmother subscribed for; one was the *Atlantic Monthly*, and, although she was often angry with it, she liked it best of all. She first read Emerson in the *Atlantic*, and she always read the editor's articles by William

Dean Howells. She was alternately infuriated and delighted with Howells, and when she was infuriated she called him "that man." I do not know why he affected her one way or the other; he had given up the editorship long before I was born; I simply know that fifty years later she would suddenly disagree with something he had said about Philadelphia.

When Grandmother heard that William Dean Howells had joined another magazine called *Harper's Monthly*, she subscribed for it, too, just to see what that man would do next. These two magazines, the *Atlantic* and *Harper's*, were Grandmother's perennial reading matter. She purchased books by their authors, and, whether she agreed or disagreed, she used their critical notices as her shopping list.

Grandmother has always been firmly in favor of the classic style in writing. Writing and thinking should be pure and precise. There was Gibbon, and then there were some others, like Emerson and Irving, who could write well, too. If anyone in her hearing had suggested, as Havelock Ellis later did, that Waldo Emerson technically wrote in a decadent style, Grandmother would have regarded Mr. Ellis as a bewildered offspring of one of Mr. Howells' worst moments; and then she would have been sure to subscribe for everything he wrote, to see what nonsense *he* wrote next.

While Grandmother has respected wisdom with a reasonable amount of awe, she never advocated education; indeed, she has been skeptical of its efforts. For some reason Grandmother always has thought of education in terms of Mr. Brown, and whenever she thought of Mr. Brown she became a little alarmed to think that she had once respected that man. Mr. Brown had represented himself as the personification of education, and Grandmother had accepted him completely; but she had later surprised him with clay feet, and she became sincerely ashamed of the dismaying influence he had had upon her.

Mr. Brown was appointed principal of the Ward School in the place of a dusty little old woman who had died, and his coming called the town's attention, for he walked down the street or entered a parlor like learning itself. He was a scholar, one could see at a glance. A short man, thick as a tub, he dressed in bishop's black with a black silk watch band across his rolling waist. Mr. Brown was a very impressive sight from the front of him, for his face was huge and grave with learning and he moved forward with a heavy, irresistible flow, like a thick, rich gravy. But in retreating, the broad Mr. Brown gave himself away, especially if his hat was off, for he had at the back of his head a bald spot that unfortunately looked like the bottom of an upturned baby. Mr. Brown's conversation was a composition of great care. He talked as though he were writing, with his sentences long and elaborate and punctuated with pauses. If his statements had by some process appeared on paper, they would have been spotted with erasures, for he thoughtfully corrected his words when he regarded them as wrong usage. His language was impressive and refreshingly free from the idiom of the West. Whenever for lack of a formal word he used slang, he always introduced it by explaining, "As you say in the West," and then he would speak the slang expression. He always chuckled in a heavy, solid roast-beef manner after he had used slang, as though the speaking of it was a quiet joke that only he could really appreciate. But, coming from him, the slang seemed limp, as though he had chewed it first.

In no time at all Mr. Brown became Virginia City's favorite guest. No reception was complete without him. In those days, after the World War, Nevada people had become conscious of the length of the nation. They began to suspect there were other good places to live besides Virginia City. Mr. Brown could speak of other places and their cultures, and the ladies were anxious to hear of them, for he seemed to know so much. They questioned him, and, if he seemed to regard their questions as silly, they laughed in embarrassment. The men did not seem so eagerly ambitious. They nodded to Mr. Brown with respect, but avoided him.

Grandmother herself dreaded asking Mr. Brown a question, for he immediately gave it his solemn attention, answering slowly and painfully, as though a casual question were of first importance and called for his concentration. Yet he somehow gave the impression that while he bulged with learning he was reluctant to let too much of it go. His answer came in such slow sentences, with such groping in his mind for appropriate words, that Grandmother from force of habit supplied him with the right word. Mr. Brown would look delicately irritated, perhaps even cough slightly, and then he would begin groping all over again until he found still another word.

He impressed Grandmother with his education, though, just as he won the respect and envy of everyone else in Virginia City. He was accepted as an authority on all matters, for he knew the exact dates of historical events, he knew how to pronounce the names of Greek playwrights and Russian novelists, and he had obviously read everything they had written. Mr. Brown was better than an encyclopedia, and Virginia City embraced him with awe. He had complete permission to supervise the school as he pleased, and he supervised it very sternly indeed. He believed that young minds should become exact minds, and he wanted his students to know all the facts. He wanted facts for answers, and to get them he taught only facts. We had to memorize facts, reducing our studies to statements of issue and dates. Dates seemed to be vital, especially the dates of conquests, battles, and assassinations. We knew the day and the hour and the place of the stabbing of Caesar, but we were never told the reason. I seemed to think it was some of Shakespeare's mischief.

Mr. Brown taught the eighth grade, but he also taught history and English to us in the fifth grade. Unlike our teachers, who sat at their desks, he stood before the class, usually with one distracting hand caressing the lapel of his coat. He stood in the same place for an hour and never seemed to shift his weight. We used to try to anticipate when he would shift from one foot to the other, but it seemed as though he never would. He referred to us as ladies and gentlemen, all of us, including Red Collins, who that afternoon was going to beat up his brother Petey, and even including Patrick Ryan, who alternated his time between the fifth grade and the Gold Hill Jail.

Mr. Brown was obviously out of place in Nevada. He continued to wear low shoes, for one thing; and he must have had a harassed life keeping dust from his white collar and black suit. He refrained from attending picnics, and he never once accepted a man's in-

vitation to come on into the Crystal for a drink; and
he displayed repugnance when Jimmy Blair, with
wonderful skill, skinned a striped lizard at recess. Mr.
Brown refused the gift of the skin, too, and that hurt
Jimmy's feelings.

Soon after Mr. Brown's coming, our room got a
plaster of Paris bust of a person he referred to as a
classical scholar; Dr. Johnson, I think it was. The bust
sat firmly over the blackboard at the front of the room,
near the flag, where it could frown down on the students. As the weeks went by and Mr. Brown no longer
indicated Dr. Johnson in his illustrations of scholar-
ship, the bust took on a yellowed, doughy look from
haphazard wipings of the janitor's cloth, and in time
it had many fly specks. But the bust continued to dis-
tinguish our room from all the others.

The other classrooms were almost exactly alike,
large rooms with desks row on row, with the seat of
the desk ahead fastened on the front of the desk behind. Underneath the surface of each desk was a shelf
for the student's books and pencils and chalk. The
teacher's desk was at the front of the room, either in
the middle or on the side by the window. Teacher's
desk usually had a bouquet of geraniums, or at least
a geranium, and sometimes there was an apple on the
desk for the class to see, brought by some admiring
student. The desk itself was something of a mystery

inside. We suspected it still contained the articles confiscated from distracted scholars, and all through the semester we wondered if teacher were going to give them back to us for our summer vacation.

Mr. Brown did not retain the articles he had confiscated. He threw them into the waste basket distastefully, even if they were perfectly good spinning-tops. Still, some of the girls brought Mr. Brown apples.

In the sixth grade in those days the girls were still given to long curls and bright ribbons. They were a scrawny, awkward lot, our girls, and when they were not giggling they were grimly intent on getting an education. Girls did not seem to come to school for the same reason boys did, because they had to. Mr. Brown seemed to realize this, and he handled the boys with extra severity. He would threaten us with his fountain pen, pointing it at us like an awful forefinger. It was the first fountain pen I ever saw, and it was a very fine, fat, black one that as a rule was pinned importantly to his vest.

In his effort to produce young ladies and gentlemen, Mr. Brown requested our parents to refrain from sending us to school in overalls. This was a tactical error, and it directed Grandmother's first spear of suspicion. All of us boys wore overalls, although some of our families were poor and some were, as we called them, well off. But the West has always been self-consciously democratic, and overalls were the accepted uniform for young boys. They were ugly, awkward things, those overalls, of blue coarse cloth all in one piece, with a bib, and held together by suspenders which had brass fasteners. For one, I was glad to be out of them. But Mr. Brown, in his ambition, caused confusion among the mothers, who had to buy their sons knickers and shirt waists and long stockings. It meant more ironing, for one thing; and that alone jeopardized Mr. Brown's position. Grandmother, at any rate, thought Mr. Brown had gone too far.

The sight of us in knickers and shirt waists, with trouser legs down and little strings hanging from our waists, must have been fairly pleasant to Mr. Brown when he rang the bell in the mornings. Before the coming of Mr. Brown, the students who had good grades had been allowed in turn to ring the large bell that was in the steeple, by tugging at its rope which hung in the building's entrance. But Mr. Brown preferred to ring the bell himself, perhaps because by doing it himself he could ring it at the precise minute, nine in the morning, not one tick one way or the other; and perhaps because he just liked to ring the bell.

Mr. Brown had also decided to set a good example in saluting the flag, and he led all of us in the salute, while we were lined out front along the hard-packed granite-dust courtyard. Mr. Brown saluted briskly, but men the shape of Mr. Brown should never be brisk; all that dignity of weight can then become jelly; Mr. Brown himself was very gratifying to look at indeed with his back to the class, saluting the flag with his black-felt hat at his feet and the bald spot on his head visible, and his chubby arm cocked to bring his hand to his forehead, and his voice as sternly dreadful as patriotism itself.

The sight seemed to inspire one of the girls who had artistic inclinations, and later, when we had gone in to class, she drew a picture of Mr. Brown without his clothes on. The serious inaccuracy and extravagance of the drawing so overwhelmed the boy who sat behind her that he laughed very loudly. It was a high-pitched, nervous, loud laugh; one shriek, and that was all. But that was enough. Mr. Brown flowed down the aisle like Fate, demanded whatever that was Marguerite had hidden in her desk, and he got it. After a look that made him gasp, he took the drawing to his desk, folded it and, without a word to the weeping, terrified girl, went on with the lesson. The next day the girl was gone. We heard that she was sent to a correction school at Reno or somewhere; we never heard of her again.

Mr. Brown taught us our lessons in stilted and elegant English that was very impressive. It made us rather proud of him, for no other teacher—no one else in town, for that matter—could speak such big English as Mr. Brown; but, to get my lesson, I had to reduce his statements to simple terms. To get good grades, however, it was necessary to recite the lesson back to Mr. Brown in an imitation of his big and lengthy English. That seemed to put an importance to whatever I said. It was an easy enough trick. One took what Mr. Brown had said, reduced it to one's own vocabulary and then, to recite, translated it back to Mr. Brown's English. I was very proud of Mr. Brown's vast learning and regarded my trick as very unethical; but it was necessary for me, since I was, as Mr. Brown inferred, quite a simple young man.

Most of my time in class I spent reading the history textbook; and, as a consequence, I got good grades in history. I knew the book almost word for word. I not only knew everything that the Gauls did, I knew exactly what they looked like. They were big men with whiskers that they never trimmed, and they wore small helmets and carried crude swords. They were, in fact, remarkably like the Vikings, except that the picture of the Vikings was on page 222 and the Gauls' was on page 109. My remarkable grasp of historical dates seemed to confound Mr. Brown, who could not understand why my other grades were weak while my history was practically perfect. I cherished my history test-papers, saving them all; they were annotated with marginal comments by Mr. Brown, who remarked on them with red ink from his fine fountain pen that they were "an excellent set of notes" or "historically accurate to the letter."

Still, even the perfection of my history grades was interrupted by my final examination, when I wrote that the Gauls were somewhat like the pioneers who came to Nevada, pillaging and arranging a state of barbarism that would finally turn into civilization. With the pleasure of a pundit, I dragged in the incident of Brennus sacking Rome and repeated how he threw his sword on the scales and cried, "Woe to the vanquished!" The pioneers, I said, were very much like Brennus. Mr. Brown marked the answer as incorrect; opposite my handsome little essay on Brennus and Pioneers he put a large red question mark. And my perfect score for the year was ruined.

Knowing better than to speak to Mr. Brown, I brought my complaints home to Grandmother. I repeated the story of the Gauls, indicated the chapter in the textbook, and showed her how in my test-paper I had written of the pioneers just as she had told me they were. Grandmother studied the problem and decided that I was right and Mr. Brown was wrong. Having come to the conclusion quickly, she thought it best to investigate further into the Gauls. The more

she read, the more convinced she was that something
was wrong with Mr. Brown. Grandmother talked
about it as if she knew a Gaul personally. A Gaul
wasn't only a name in the history book and a picture
on page 109, he was an individual with strong char-
acteristics who might have walked down C Street the
other day. Grandmother came to several conclusions.
One was that Mr. Brown had not stimulated my curiosity in history; indeed, she believed he had tried to
frustrate it. Another was that Mr. Brown and his red
ink had discouraged my comparing history with contemporary matters; and another, that Mr. Brown himself, as a scholar, was not curious, which was a dreadful state of affairs. For Grandmother used "curious"
to mean an awareness of things.

After these conclusions, which were belittled by the
family, who maintained Mr. Brown knew what he
was doing, Grandmother began to take an interest in
my education. Since the family defended Mr. Brown,
Grandmother was forced to defend me to protect herself. She noted the importance Mr. Brown attached to
facts, especially dates. Now Grandmother could see
no importance in dates. Herself, she placed happenings in vague eras, each era neatly bound together by
a small, timely, and probably significant event; for
example, the death of Fighting Sam Brown ended the
era of hoodlum power in Virginia City, and the World

War started on the day she rented the Johnson home. The Johnsons left their home to her when mine development in Nevada began to decline, therefore the World War and the decline of the Comstock mines began together. It was as simple as that. Grandmother didn't care whether the war started in the nineteen-hundreds or the eighties, and she couldn't see how it could matter much to anyone else.

History for her was no trouble at all. Civilization went up and down; it flourished and wilted, barbarians plucked it, the world fell into a barren, sullen age, and after being cultivated, it finally blossomed again. The dates or the particular facts did not matter to Grandmother. The important thing was that it did act this way, and it would as long as people were so slipshod.

With Grandmother attending to my studies, education became increasingly difficult. Where before I had had to recite the facts to Mr. Brown, now I also had to give them an interpretation for Grandmother. My school day was just getting started when supper was over. Grandmother sat in her rocker in the sitting room, and I was on a footstool at her feet. For an hour our only interruption was a reference to the textbook or my getting up to put wood in the fire.

It happened by a coincidence unfortunate for Mr. Brown that he brought our study to Julius Caesar in

English and history at the same time. We were reading about what he did to Rome while we were reading Shakespeare's version of him. Grandmother noticed several disagreements between what Shakespeare said of him and what Mr. Brown said. Grandmother was inclined to believe Shakespeare. While Mr. Brown spoke of the legions of Caesar and the triumphs of him, Shakespeare sighed with his tragic life, and so did Grandmother.

Grandmother and Mr. Brown became enemies because of Julius Caesar, although neither knew it for some time. Mr. Brown spoke of the strength of Rome and the might of Caesar, and Grandmother noted that Caesar lived by a tragic philosophy and that his end was bound to be unpleasant. Caesar became an illustration and an example for Grandmother. She noticed that he gave his life to acquisition and aggression, but that he was certain to fail finally because his philosophy had a hole in it. Inasmuch as he had given his life to acquisition, power and possessions were his treasures; but a man, she believed, who wanted power could never get enough of it, and he could never take it with him when he died, which was proof to Grandmother that Caesar lived for wrong purposes. While he was mighty, taking what he pleased and going where he wanted, he was also a rather foolish man who had gone just too far. Grandmother saw a remarkable resemblance between him and the Nevada nabobs, the mining financiers who had developed the Comstock. They grasped power, yet they never seemed to know quite what to do with it. Both John Mackay and George Hearst were vivid in Grandmother's mind, and their extravagant investments were still spoken of with awe in Virginia City. With Grandmother's interpretation, Julius Caesar for me became a sort of mining man with great energy, many crews of men, and much gold.

Caesar's career was malleable enough under Grandmother's interpretation for her to use it as an example of nearly anything. His career fairly summed up the pioneers for her. They had come to the Comstock aggressive and acquisitive as Caesars, and they worked hard to get all they could from the ground.

"Here," she said, "is their weakness, for it must have made them most unhappy to die and be unable to take their gold with them back to the ground."

In a sense, my grandmother in summing up the pioneers did also sum up the ambitions of the nation at that time, the period from the eighteen to the nineteen hundreds, and intentionally or unintentionally she indicated the culture we were to develop. It was happening especially in the schools. A schoolboy in the West after the World War, and I presume elsewhere in the nation, was encouraged to get himself educated as quickly as possible. He was encouraged to push himself forward, and he really could go rapidly through one grade after another if he memorized certain facts well enough to repeat them exactly in his examinations. The better he knew his facts, the better were his grades, and the sooner he was handed to the world. His education guaranteed, he was equipped to conquer a piece of the world for himself; at least, nothing was ever said of how he should fit himself into the world. With his diploma signed by the principal and the state governor, he was in himself equipped to be a Caesar. He knew that his education was his weapon.

It was not necessary for a schoolboy to form his learning into a pattern. That was done for him in school and called an education. He was given a reasonable number of facts to learn, and when he had learned them he had an education. It was as simple as that. He carried it with him not as a part that would help him to live well, but as a sword.

But even as a weapon his education was not very valuable. At the best it could serve for defense. He could read and write and put the correct answer after a column of figures; but how to use his reading and writing and arithmetic to earn a living, he did not exactly know. Since he was given as his models those who got the most money, he should have been told the details of how they did it. Having been warned to be aggressive, he should also have been told the formula for aggressiveness and given the ethics that would enable him to work his way into the circle of his superiors. That would have been the logical development of his education. Instead he was told by his teachers and by all the prominent people, those most admirable citizens who spoke at his school, that the way to succeed was to work hard, go to bed early, and be up with the birds.

This was difficult to believe for a schoolboy who had a grandmother who believed that he should not work too hard but should enjoy himself whenever he could, and who herself went to bed late and got up when she pleased and, as if to spite the public speakers, seemed to have a reasonable amount of pleasure, even without very much money.

Now that Grandmother had disagreed with Mr. Brown about Julius Caesar, she did not seem to care whether her grandson attended his classes. Indeed, she encouraged him not to worry too much about civics and the nation's judiciary system and she told him point-blank, in rigid defiance of the textbook, that the Americans were not at all practically perfect, and that something could be said for many governments.

Grandmother decided that Mr. Brown's lessons were not only useless but misleading; indeed, she finally decided they were injurious. The fact that Mr. Brown had once impressed her with his learning now made him appear heavily pretentious; and, because she had respected him, she became ashamed of herself. She felt she should have seen through him all along. At any rate, it was not too late; her grandson could disregard him.

Mother suggested cautiously that perhaps Grandmother had been hasty in her judgment, but Grandmother replied that whether she was hasty or not had nothing to do with it. The man had proven himself inadequate; that was enough. But Mother, who was a school teacher, did not like to hear Grandmother talk that way about Mr. Brown, especially before her grandson, who was just a child. Grandmother disliked such interference. She wanted to know whose child I was, anyway.

Chapter Eight

Chapter Eight

MY GRANDMOTHER REGARDS THE MOD-
ERN BATHROOM AS A MENACE. SHE
has said it is just as well none of her contemporaries
has lived to see it, such a slippery place of tile and
porcelain; it would frighten the ladies and confuse the
gentlemen. Plumbing, though, is an improvement,
she will admit; yet its values have been over-empha-
sized when one's plumbing is given a personality
and a family's proudest place becomes the bathroom. There have been sincere attempts to introduce
the modern bathroom to Grandmother, but she thinks
that in its white and purple and blue it is unfriendly
and moody, like a theatre lobby. Then one must be on
her guard against its dangers, for if a lady fell in her
bath the injury would be serious. She would at least
be bruised and humiliated, and it would be necessary
to dry and dress herself before sending a neighbor for
the doctor.

At Grandmother's house there is no bathroom, and
one bathes in the bedroom. A bath is accomplished
under strenuous and, sometimes, exciting circum-

stances, from a tub kept in a walnut box; that is, if one is a guest. If he isn't, he bathes in a tin tub.

Grandmother's bath is a rite that provokes preparation and forethought. The tub is taken from its corner, where it rests in a dark hardwood box. A fire is lighted in the bedroom fireplace; towels are laid out, and a mat is spread. A careful search of the carpet comes next for chance pins or needles, and if one is found it is placed in a silver pincushion on Grandmother's bureau. Then the wing of the house is isolated for the sake of privacy, and Grandmother's bath begins.

Grandmother is an especially immaculate person. Her skin has a cleanness that gives the effect of a bright calm, it is so clear. While Grandmother is an advocate of soap and water, she ignores the modern weapons of cleanliness; for example, the toothbrush. Instead she uses cotton cloth that has been boiled and dried. It is cut into squares precisely half the size of her handkerchiefs; and for tooth powder she uses baking soda, occasionally mixing salt with it. Grandmother does not suggest that other people should utilize the procedure, by offering as example the fact that she is ninety years of age and has retained her teeth. Indeed, such a suggestion is not for discussion. Caring for the teeth is part of bathing and is completely personal.

While Grandmother insists upon complete privacy for her bathing, she has been forced to come to the kitchen to dry her hair. That is partly a concession given years ago to her family and partly the fact that the open fireplace could throw sparks on the long strands of her hair. The kitchen is dry and warm, and there Grandmother can dry and brush her hair rapidly. Her hair falls lower than her shoulders, and the texture of it is so fine that the gray can scarcely be detected and it seems completely white. She combs it with a silver comb that she is very fond of, and dampens the comb in the basin before running it through her hair. The combing and brushing concluded, she brings the locks of her hair to a knot at the back of her head, where they are secured with a baffling network of hairpins.

Grandmother has often been cautioned never to brush her own hair. The doctor told her that it would strain her heart, lifting her hands above her head time after time. That's nonsense, Grandmother thinks. If one obeyed such absurd instructions, her time would be spent hanging on to life, but everywhere as always there would still be reminders of the grave. Besides, her heart is as sound as anyone else's. Lifting her hands, indeed! She supposes that the machine age has invented something to lift her hands for her!

As for the machine age, Grandmother regards it as

part of the nuisance of this world. She is able to get along with it only if it stays out of her way. She doesn't consider herself or Virginia City, either, as belonging or having anything to do with it. She wouldn't be surprised, though, if Virginia City relented and had a filling station.

Grandmother realizes that filling stations with their oil and gasoline are a menace, too. Not only are they likely to blow up, but they exhale fumes she doesn't like. Virginia City, being high in the mountains, has clean, light air, but a filling station would pollute it in a moment. Carbon monoxide is something she blames me for. She says my generation uses it and grows old on it, just as if it were air. Carbon monoxide may likely be more injurious than night air. As for night air, she will have none of it, either. She has taken precaution to keep it from her bedroom because she knows night air would kill anybody.

Yet Grandmother contradicts herself again by not thoroughly disliking the automobile. It is a nuisance, to be sure, and it is insolent; but it is mostly silly. It is also overrated, pretending a power it doesn't possess, for a little nail will stop it; and Heaven knows there are enough nails in Nevada. She will ride in an automobile, if she has to, but with the apprehension that something in it is about to break. In fact, she was one of the first to ride in an automobile. The event took place in the days of the Maxwell and rough roads, and the Maxwell was a large touring model. But it snorted more than most Maxwells. My grandmother, standing at the kitchen window, heard it snorting and watched the way it trembled. It looked skittish to Grandmother, but she had dressed for the ride and intended to see it through, and get it over with.

The back seat of the Maxwell, Grandmother estimated, seemed the more substantial. She sat there, very small, protected by carriage robes and a veil that hung from her hat. The hat, in turn, was steadied to her head by a long and malicious-looking pin. Grandmother sat exactly in the middle of the seat, where she was not likely to tip the car over on a turn. The clutch did not operate quietly; and the Maxwell started with a protest in the bowels of the transmission, then jumped forward, and Grandmother was gone.

Grandmother admitted the trip was rather pleasant, except for the dust and bumps. The automobile had its place in travel; but with a horse and carriage it was also possible to see the country. Since then she has often ridden in other automobiles, but always with an attitude which was faintly questioning and highly critical. She never rode again in the Maxwell, though, and when its work was done and it was left to rust and mildew behind the barn Grandmother regarded its decadence with satisfaction. It was part of the new machine age, and she had outlived it. The triumph was personal and entirely flattering.

It was automobiles that began bringing tourists to Virginia City, and Grandmother thinks tourists are terrible. With their automobiles and their horns and service station fumes, tourists to her are an indication that the world is involved in a machine age, and that it may even fall to pieces, like the old Maxwell. Grandmother is glad she is not part of so unstable an age. She knows that tourists are typical of it, and that they are the accent and haste in our time. They can't help being nervous and cranky, driving as they do all day long in their cars, but she wonders what it is precisely in their lives that makes them hurry as though they had somewhere to go.

From the beginning of spring to the end of summer Grandmother can hear motorcars groaning up Gold Hill to the Divide on their way to Virginia City. She knows that some of the automobiles will be stopped, and that the tourists will climb out to stretch and then clamber over the masses of cool, refreshing rocks. And they will call to each other from the rock tops and shout to hear the echo return from the valley reluctantly. And the ladies in trousers will spread robes on the earth and twitter over their lunches.

Grandmother learned early that tourists have a fondness for taking pictures of one another. Some-

times, too, they exclaim about her house and pose
there by the gate, arms linked and feet on the hitch-
ing-bar, as though her home were a museum or some
curiosity. Grandmother contemplates them from the
window and withdraws. She does not speak to them.
Once, while she was in the garden, a man in khaki
breeches with fat legs asked if she would like to be in
the picture. When she declined, he offered her a dollar. Grandmother was very pleased. It was just what
she could expect from a tourist.

Sometimes the passing automobiles awaken Grandmother. This exasperates her, and caused her once to
call the constable and warn him to put a stop to it.
Her morning sleep must not be disturbed. Grandmother's day does begin late in the morning, for she
dislikes early rising. When she was very young and
a wife she had to rise early to start the children for
school, and she said she could never feel civilized getting up in the dark. Virginia City, for the most part,
arises at dawn, but not Grandmother. Eleven o'clock
is a decent time, and much before ten o'clock is absolutely savage. Now that she is alone, she is shielded
from criticism for her late rising. In the days when
she had servants she arose late anyway, after the
house had been thoroughly warmed, and such a custom seemed to infuriate her neighbors, for they talked
of it indignantly, seeming to regard Grandmother's

late rising as an affront to themselves and to decency.

Grandmother always had her breakfast alone, when the family had finished; she began with fruit, then had an egg, eaten slowly—preferably a soft-boiled egg with a slice of dry toast—and ended with at least two cups of coffee.

Breakfast for the rest of the family was a hurried and uncommunicative meal, with the chair left vacant that Grandmother was to occupy later. Frank, her eldest son, would be at the head of the table, at a place reserved for him by a silver napkin-ring which had his name engraved upon it. He would have mush and fruit, two eggs and bacon, toast and coffee and then pie, for he was six feet three and he had heavy work to do. He was fourteen when his father died, and he had been forced into the mines. He wanted to be something else—a civil engineer if he could—but he started being a miner and he couldn't seem to stop. Grandmother and he had a hard time of it raising the family; Frank working as a pick-boy, and Grandmother sewing and sometimes acting as a nurse. Frank, despite himself, became a very good miner. At twenty-one he had his own crew of men and he was making small and timid investments in silver stock. At twenty-two he was consulted about the value of drifts and pockets in the mine; and at twenty-three, when it looked as though he would be able to work his way out of the mine, he was killed by a cave-in.

This left as the eldest son, Edward, who sat next to Frank at the table. Edward refused to be a miner but studied enough engineering to operate hoisting motors. Then he quit studying. He said he knew all he wanted to know about mines. He was a very difficult man for Virginia City to understand. He had a garden, for one thing; and a garden in Virginia City, in such a dry and sullen land, was preposterous. But a garden it was, and it required all his leisure to attend to it. While he was in school he helped support the family with vegetables from his garden. He also grew flowers that had to be nursed through a ground so harsh it had thin cracks in it and a surface soil like crumbled granite. For his favorite flowers he purchased topsoil from California, from a place that is now named Burbank, and he had to submit to endless inconvenience to get it past the border of a state which was suspicious of everything that came from California, especially if it were the very soil. Edward built a wall around his garden, and in the evening, before the wind came, he spread canvas over it.

Edward had a crab-apple tree which was his very pride. As a special gesture he would sometimes let me pick an apple. I wasn't allowed to choose one at my own invitation, for he knew exactly how many apples his tree had; and he could be unpleasant about a missing one. Second in importance to the tree was Edward's turkey. That turkey, too, was preposterous. Edward had carried an egg to a ten-thousand-foot level in the mine and placed it on a warm rock. Twice a day he turned the egg. This was before the use of incubation, and the miners looked at Edward and each other, and tapped their foreheads knowingly.

But the egg hatched and Edward found himself a hero. In proper time he carried his turkey to the surface, up the steel hoist and through the timbered caverns, his bird bundled in his greatcoat; and they both met photographers from as far away as San Francisco. The picture of the turkey was put on postcards, and the miners mailed them to friends in the East, who must have been reasonably dubious.

The family understood that Edward would not live long. He was never very strong, was the explanation for Edward. He was more nimble of mind and analytical than his brothers, though, and he was the only one who shared Grandmother's penetrating wit. Edward was rather a small man; at least, he was for his family, being two heads shorter than his brothers; but he was feared. Although he was gentle-looking with a roundish face and kinky hair, he frightened his brothers because he knew them so well. He could prick their pride, or as a punishment deflate it entirely; he knew their ulterior motives. They said of him, "You can't keep *anything* from Edward."

When the World War came and his brothers said they wanted to enlist, Edward told them that people were fools who wanted to be soldiers.

"Everyone realizes," he said, "that deaths are common in war; but everyone likewise believes that he will be an exception and come home in triumph. Well, wars do one good anyway. A battlefield must cultivate the richest tomatoes."

While his brothers could be fighting men, and thus respected, Edward could be terrifying, attacking with sharp words, brave and honest, that penetrated his opponents and reduced them to mutters. The Comstock miners liked to argue and spent evenings on the sidewalk confounding each other with theories; but Edward would never argue, because he never found a man who knew what he was talking about. Facing him, the miners became inarticulate and took to awkward gesturing. People said that some day an angry miner would hit Edward and kill him, but of course no miner ever did.

Indeed, he died peacefully when he was fifty years old, after an illness that had been not too lingering and left him clear-headed to the last. He left without protest, and Grandmother said that he was the strongest of her sons.

Albert was the youngest brother, and he looked upon Frank at the head of the table as some sort of substitute parent. Albert was tall and graceful, with straight black hair that he proudly parted far on one side. He had the very fine skin of his mother and the strength of his father, and he had a friendliness that let everyone accept and like him. Yet he lived a tragic life.

Albert was caught by the World War and badly wounded, but he returned to Virginia City to be in a mining explosion that crushed his leg and broke his hip. He lived his middle years in a hospital, learning to walk again; in time he did recover, but he was crushed again in a second explosion, losing forever the strength in his arms.

When Albert was released from the hospital in San Francisco, he did not want to return to Virginia City. He retreated to a high place in Nevada, where he leased the top of a mountain with his pension and lived alone. It was almost impossible for anyone to visit Albert whom he did not wish to see, for a visitor could neither walk nor drive up the mountain, but could get there only on horseback on one of Albert's horses that knew the trail. There were not many friends that he wanted to see.

Albert finally came back to the Comstock to joke

at what he called his damned foolishness. But there was little for him to do except remain in the house, and he died less than a year afterward, after having lived with pneumonia ten days longer than the doctors said he could, which seemed to please him.

The fourth person at the table was my mother. She was a girl then, at the turn of the century, the baby of the family, but not the only daughter for she had a sister who was already married and had a child of her own and lived with her husband farther down the Divide. Mother, being the last child, had the advantage. There were three brothers to send her to college, and they saw to it that she stayed in college; and when she was graduated, they managed to get her a school to teach close by.

When breakfast was over and the table cleared, Grandmother would probably be having her morning chocolate. Around the house the word would go that Grandmother was almost ready to get up. Disarray was straightened, the stove was looked to, and arguments came to an end. Grandmother walked into the dining room for breakfast, very small and slim-looking in her dressing gown, her hair brushed back and temporarily secured by a net. While she was small and fragile and much too feminine to be formidable, there was no mistaking that the home now had some one in charge, and an authority to decide the day's problems and outline what was to be purchased for dinner and supper.

Dinner was at one o'clock for the family, but not for Grandmother, who had housework to do. But after dinner, when the family was gone again, there were three long and leisurely hours in the sitting room, where perhaps she was sewing or reading. The afternoons were pleasant, for they were something of a recess. Perhaps there would be a visitor for tea, but if not there were always tasks that could be done pleasantly, sewing to be done or letters to be answered. The sun was almost sure to be shining through the large side window, and it would make the curtains look fresh and light and throw a cheerful reflection across the room.

The afternoon was interrupted surely by the stir of supper time. The sons came home from work with their coats under their arms if the weather was warm, and swinging their dinner pails and calling goodbye at the gate to friends who had farther to go. Edward would change to his boots and go out to sprinkle the garden, and Albert saw to the horses. Grandmother would be in the kitchen, supervising the supper.

This was the anxious hour of the day for a young boy who had been playing most of the morning and reading and napping in the afternoon. Supper was such a long time coming. Edward would linger over his flowers, and Albert would find something wrong with a horse. There was a good deal of time for him to sit by the fire in the kitchen, where he was wonderfully in the way, but with his face scrubbed in accordance with Grandmother's law, his overalls put aside for a shirt waist, bow tie, and knickers, and with his shoes polished—but not brightly, for Grandmother disapproved of shined shoes, no matter how much her grandson favored them. All this preparation was necessary if the boy was to be allowed to have his supper with the family, instead of being placed in bed after milk and cookies and an apple.

Supper was the time for the telling of the day's anecdotes, just as certainly as after supper was the time for peace and quiet that lasted all of an hour. By evening there was always the delightful chance that guests would call, which made staying up all the better for the boy. If they were friends, not parlor guests, then there would be strange and wonderful words about the government or things that happened in Carson City. There would be lengthy and elaborate opinions politely given and politely received, different opinions from those one heard in his own house; and they would be followed by a murmur of appreciation with everyone thinking-so-too. Perhaps an opinion would bring a slight discord of agreement. Then everyone argued in turn except Grandmother, who would just listen or nod while she sewed. But she would be the one to say when the sherry should appear, and whether there was to be cake cut.

My favorite of the guests was Roark Taylor. He was a young man, Albert's age, and usually a quiet man, but he could tell fine stories if I were the only one listening. He had never been away from Nevada; but he had read of other places, and he liked to talk about them as though he had been there. He would talk about the height of buildings in the cities and the ships that crossed the sea, and of a man who had been an actor and had gone around the world meeting new people and seeing far places. Roark was a prospector, but he did not like it very well. He thought he would like to be a writer; if he couldn't be a writer, he would be a teacher. But first he had to go away to college. Not just to Reno—that was for mining engineers—but to a college back East, where his family came from. He did not yet have the money to go, but he was saving his money. When he was twenty-five he would leave; he had that settled.

Roark knew better than to talk to me about mining. I liked to have him tell me about cowboys and the real red Indians, not the Piutes we had in Nevada. I never considered Piutes to be real Indians; at least, they weren't like the Mohicans that Roark and I read about. There was too much talk about mining anyway. All the people that visited us except Roark talked about it. They might start talking about other things, but after a while it would surely be mining and miners, and I would rather hear about cowboys. Still, listening was better than going to bed.

Grandmother was the last of us to go to bed. She had to put on her shawl and go out to the woodshed to be sure that the dog and the pigeons were comfortable and that the snowshed door was bolted. The rest of us went right to bed when the guests left, Frank and Albert winding their clocks and comparing them with their watches, and Edward carefully laying out the clothes that he would wear tomorrow. But Grandmother usually sat by the fire long after we were asleep. And always she would have Albert light the fireplace in her bedroom and bring in plenty of wood, and she would sit there in her rocking chair and read, sometimes until dawn. I knew, because whenever I awakened I could see the ribbon of light under her door; yet in the morning when she was asked if she had slept well, she would say she had dropped right off to sleep shortly after midnight and did not stir until the sun awakened her.

Chapter Nine

Chapter Nine

FOR AT LEAST THE LAST TEN YEARS MOST OF GRANDMOTHER'S INCOME HAS come from selling her possessions. In her life she had collected many things that were valuable, but the amount of her attachment to them decreased with the years until finally she really didn't care to possess objects any more. They had been jewelry, partly, for people in the West owned jewelry for one of two purposes: to display their wealth or to invest it. In a land where money was gold and silver, and even banks avoided bank notes, jewels were a very sound security. Whether one wore or hid them, they were a weapon against times of trouble.

Grandmother had some precious stones that had not been cut and polished, rubies and emeralds, a few; and she had many *specimens* of ore, cuts of quartz that were threaded with silver and gold. These were called "hygrade," either because they were high in value or because they contained two metals. In the early days of mining each crew of workers was allowed to set aside the pieces of hygrade, which were placed in a sack. At the end of each working shift the men were allowed to take a piece with them as they filed from the mine. But in times to come, when financiers from the East controlled the mines, the practice was forbidden, and hygrading became a criminal offense.

But at the first Grandmother had collected many specimens that her husband brought home. Some of them were given away to friends in the East who had asked what gold looked like in the ground, but most of them she kept in a grocery box in the harness room; and one fine specimen the size and shape of a sitting cat, she had polished to use to hold open the dining-room door. She realized it was valuable stone, but then there were many valuable stones: the earth was filled with them. A man from New York offered her twenty-five dollars for it, but that was in the nineteenth century, and she refused it; she finally sold it a few years later for three hundred dollars.

It was not until the last ten years, though, that Grandmother began selling her belongings. With Virginia City deserted and her family gone, she no longer needed her property; but she did need the little money that it could bring. She sold specimens first, and then she sold the furniture in her houses to antique collectors; and she sold most of it piece by piece to get the better price for it. Grandmother had plenty of

furniture to sell, for when families left the Divide
their homes were usually sold to her or put in her
trust to rent or lease. She had been on the Divide
when most of the families came to Virginia City, and,
because she was there when they left, they assumed
she would always be there. She was the recognized
first resident, and although she was a little difficult to
understand with her firm and quaint opinions, she had
become the one to consult about Virginia City and its
property.

I do not know exactly how the people felt about
Grandmother, but when I was a boy they enquired
often about her. No one called her by her first name,
although so many of them had been with her for years.
Indeed, I have never heard anyone mention her first
name, although people like the Dwights and Taylors
had been her friends for thirty years. I, too, was under
the domination of Grandmother's name and seldom
heard my surname mentioned. I was Master Flannery, the Flannery boy, and even Mrs. Flannery's
boy.

Candidates for public office consulted Grandmother,
and although she scarcely knew one from another, or
for what offices they were candidates, they must have
felt it advantageous to call upon her and leave their
cards in the tray in the hallway. I recall that she seldom called upon anyone. Although she would say she

must return that young woman's visit or the call to the new school teacher, she very seldom did; but people understood and came again.

Grandmother must have had thirty to forty houses. The number can be estimated only approximately because by now most of them have been torn down and sold for their wood. But in their times they had been important homes, large and often elaborate, each of them with seven to ten rooms, and adjoining them were barns and sheds for poultry and livestock, and the backs of the yards were enclosed by corrals for the horses. They would have been ranch houses if the architecture had not been thinly New England. The roofs were sloping and had been rubbed raw by sliding snows. The houses in this high place could not be protected by trees or embraced by vines, but stood bare and bruised yet still formidable, very wooden and serious houses that had been planted abruptly in the harsh earth. Such homes seemed depressing, painted as they were in vague grays and browns, with cheerless, formal fronts as though inside lived unaffectionate people. They were out of place in Nevada, these awkward and expensive frame buildings from the nineteenth century of the East that tried to be genteel in a vigorous land.

Down below in Virginia City the homes had been built one against another, for they clung to the low side of Mt. Davidson and their owners wanted them close, as though they had been braced together. The homes on the Divide, however, had been built later by the people who always want to be above the majority, and because their homes were suburban they were more spacious. The Divide stood on the mountain top, barely above Virginia City on one side and Gold Hill on the other, an island surrounded by mines. Mt. Davidson towered over the Divide on the west, and on the east another mountain rolled away to a wilderness of scrub pines and sagebrush.

Much of the Divide, like Virginia City and Gold Hill, had fallen away by the twentieth century. There were half a hundred houses and then acres of cleared ground with the wooden squares that had been the foundations of buildings. One of the buildings that for some reason still stood was a five-room home made of tin. It was rusty when I saw it, but Grandmother said that once it had been painted a bright blue, for it had been the idea of a young couple who came from California without the money to build a wood house.

The families were leaving the Divide and the city as the century turned and the mines began closing. Wages in the mines that were still operated had been lowered, for the owners had come to the last of the Big Bonanza veins and the small drifts the miners had to follow brought the owners less profit. A migration of Mexicans came from the silver mines below the border and drove away the pioneers, who refused to work, they protested, alongside greasers. They were good miners, the Mexicans, although the Americans loudly denied it. The Americans, though they, too, worked with pick and shovel, regarded themselves as craftsmen. But the Mexicans were common laborers.

The Americans, who had come to the Comstock first, somehow believed they were in a world of their own. Their superiors were miners who could "smell ore" in a rock, and their inferiors were the mill workers on the surface. The rest of the world was busy with occupations that didn't matter. It was not the miners who were isolated from the world: the rest of the world was isolated from the miners, and so far as Virginia City knew, the happenings in other places had not the slightest effect upon them. They were in Virginia City simply to dig the gold; after the trains carried it away, their concern with the ore was over, and they did not care what happened to it. Of course, there were problems about the gold standard, and some talk, too, about a silver standard, but all this was just in the newspapers. For themselves, their concern was the gold in the ground, and when that became scarce they realized for the first time that their world could not last forever.

No one had saved his wages, for more wages were

always coming. One could spend all his money on a good table and homes and celebration, for there was a payday next week. Life was fast and rich and reasonably good, and a miner was glad to be living it. He had many children, for that was the thing to do, and, besides, children just came along anyway. The more children he had, the more sons to work in the mines, the more daughters to help his wife. He needed them because a miner wasn't his best after forty; he was happy in his assurance of having his sons working beside him.

When the wage scale dropped, the families could not of their own accord lower their standard of living. They had to wrench themselves loose and move on, which is how Grandmother came to purchase their homes. It is good that she did, for now that even her sons have been buried, she needs a source for an income. It was a risk, buying the houses, but her husband had often told her that the mining companies were following only the veins of silver and were even discarding ore that was heavy with gold dust. Those mountains of discarded ore were piled thick around the city. She was pretty sure that they would be milled, which would mean work for quite a few years.

Grandmother rented her places to the laborers who followed after the pioneers. The comfort of the homes should have gratified them, because they were now getting the reward that the original owners had intended for their children. Pioneers were willing to work hard to build a city and homes as a civilization for their children to enjoy, but in this case it was the Mexicans and untrained workmen with their families who got the benefit. Indeed, some of the most elaborate homes became Mexican boarding houses, and a sight it must have been to Grandmother, too, to see the laborers dozing on the wide porches in the evening, with their shoes off and overalls unbuttoned, with the large gray homes behind them frowning as they dozed with an expression of extreme comfort on their dark faces.

The migration of Mexicans continued for the next two decades, as laborers worked awhile and moved on. The mountains of discarded ore were milled, and abandoned mines were retimbered and worked again, and Grandmother kept her houses rented. Gradually, though, as the gold became increasingly scarce and fewer men were working, it became difficult for Grandmother to rent all the places.

Some of her houses had to be torn down and sold for lumber because they had begun to sink into the earth. The entire Comstock district, from Virginia City to Gold Hill, had been so completely undermined that the level of the earth fell away gradually for a length of ten miles. Some houses sank five feet or so, until their porches were a step below the street and their cellars were gone completely.

In the early days, when property was very valuable indeed, a house owner could sell the mining rights to his land; and he usually cheerfully did, believing that because the mines were already down thousands of feet and going deeper daily, his home way up on the surface would never be disturbed. The money he received for the mining rights was simply a gift from misled Eastern financiers, people he would gladly cheat anyway. But the mines took the backbone from the earth, and the surface slowly slipped down until now some houses have sunk with it over their heads to the rooftops.

Of course, Grandmother's home has not sunk a bit. She refused to sell the mining rights to it or to any of her surrounding property. Her refusals were regarded by the family as ridiculous, but just like Grandmother. The mines had the right to tunnel their way a few hundred feet beneath her property, but they were not allowed to raise their tunnels higher. Grandmother was warned that she had better sell or the mines would take the mining rights away from her anyway; but, as it turned out, the ground beneath her was free of gold.

Something told her, Grandmother said, that the companies weren't buying property unless they intended to mine it. Despite the confidence of her neighbors that the rights had been purchased as a precaution only, Grandmother felt there was an ulterior motive somewhere, and she wasn't going to sell until she discovered it. As a result, her home must be the only one on the Divide that has been undisturbed. Indeed, it must be the only one that still has its furniture, but it doesn't have all the furniture that was brought with such grumblings over the Sierra Nevadas.

Grandmother sold her parlor furnishings first. The highboy with the shining miniatures on it went away with an antique collector from San Francisco. He came to the side door one day, a little man in a neat black suit with a calming manner to him. He had heard, he said, that this time Mrs. Flannery had some of her own furniture for sale. Perhaps as a collector he could see some of it anyway. He followed Grandmother into the parlor and stood there, his hat in his hand, respectful but matter-of-fact. He appraised the furniture with confident glances and murmured politely in appreciation of the whatnot. People in California were buying whatnots like that, he said. If Mrs. Flannery did not need it any more, he would be glad to purchase it.

Grandmother said she had no use for the foolish thing. Besides, as she realized, the original furniture in the houses she owned had already been sold and even most of the houses themselves were gone. She admitted the whatnot had a price, and when the collector mentioned his right price, Grandmother looked at him and smiled. The collector smiled, too, and named her price; and he got the whatnot and the mementos that went along with it.

In other months the collector came again until finally the parlor was bare. Grandmother did not especially regret selling her furniture, for she is not an acquisitive person. Virginia City was acquisitive and aggressive, but Grandmother as she grew older cared less for possession of material things. She was probably glad to be rid of the parlor, for so many of the uncomfortable moments of her life had been in there. The people she had to receive, the attorneys who made settlement—they came to the parlor. It was not pleasant to sit in there alone; it was so very quiet and close with the heavy furniture. The dead, too, had been brought there briefly, to be seen and wept for. Grandmother had sat in there one night by her husband's body, in the dark with a robe about her legs, waiting for morning and the priest to come. I imagine Grandmother realized there would be a night when she, like her husband and sons, would be detained in the parlor briefly with the door closed and the house hushed.

Grandmother always associated her parlor with her inability to appreciate the people in the West, and she considered it as an inappropriate part of pioneer life. The parlor was instead a belonging of an older land, where the family had more distinctions and traditions. It had a definite place in her home in her childhood in New England, for there the parlor was the showcase for the family, deliberately set apart from the living rooms so that it could be always formal and perhaps formidable. It was the room a visitor was led into before he was accepted as a friend, where he was on display to prove himself, to be accepted or rejected; or the parlor was where the family was proving itself. The room belonged to everyone in the house, to the three generations. The grandmothers and the mothers and their daughters could count and rely upon it, for it gave gossip the elegance of discussion; it could frustrate familiarity, and it offered the young gentleman a chance to propose.

As a girl Grandmother had learned to know people in their two standards, for what they were and what they were in their parlors. Her father supported a magnificently pretentious parlor, with thick books bound in maroon and stamped with the family bookplate, but with type so small it could scarcely be read. It had furniture that stood with heavy gloom and austerity, and its paintings had the very best gilt frames. Her father's parlor indicated, therefore, that the family was a member of the upper middle class and the best the town in New England had to offer. As a girl, Grandmother in her conduct had to live up to her parlor, and as she grew older the parlor would have graduated her into an established resident of the community, entitled her to quiet respect and, in the end, a most solemn funeral. If she had stayed in New England, her father's parlor would have seen to it that she and her husband became the stern, strong force that maintained the character of the community, kept the schools in order and the laborers working, and chosen the representatives to elect the President to guide the nation. Since she and her husband would have had to represent themselves as formidably as their parlor, their lives would have been an example for the town to follow. For setting an example and keeping it, they would have expected to influence the future, and the future would have taken care of their children.

Grandmother thought that her parlor in the West, while less ornate, was even more pretentious. Its purpose was to maintain a culture that was in another land, but hybrid in this one, for it represented standards and traditions that did not survive the crossing of the continent. But people in Virginia City had a parlor if they had a house; and one parlor was remarkably like another, and none had the distinction of its family. Pioneers are all of one class to Grandmother. They may have come from many places, but when they are banded together in a common purpose, they are a large and sprawling society with the same ambitions and frustrations.

The purposes of pioneers, Grandmother believes, have been misunderstood; she will give pioneers her admiration but not her respect. They are courageous, and she admires them for it, but courage is so often a blind quality that she thinks they are no more courageous and progressive because they struck out for a new land than if they had stayed in the old. They have her sympathy because they are misfits unable to adjust themselves to an established society. They feel the necessity to move on to another land, which is a feeling that she appreciates. But they seem tragically maladjusted to Grandmother because, after having moved once, they move again, forever moving and changing to break up friendships and their children's education, forever moving and changing the pattern of their lives because they never seem to fit in.

Grandmother regrets that the pioneers who searched for new land cherished it so little when they found it. When she looks from her window, she can see on the hillsides the stumps of the trees they cut down, the dry ravines that had their waters side-streamed, and the acres of discarded ore that could have been cultivated. The pioneers that she knew failed to replenish the land, and when the trees and the water and gold were gone, they were surprised and unprepared, and forced to move on.

These were the people who came to Grandmother's parlor. Their interest was in the mining that would make them wealthy. While Grandmother, too, wanted wealth, she also wanted Virginia City to be developed into a city of many industries. The land around it could have been easily cultivated for farming and ranching, and that would have made Virginia City substantial and permanent enough to care for her children when she and her husband were gone. But the city had been for gold only and, having been drained of its spectacular wealth, was of no use further. Her husband had passed along, and even her children, and marriage had taken away the last one, her youngest daughter, who could not have a future in such a place as Virginia City. The original settlers who had remained in the Comstock had died long ago, and the second generation was gone, too; and the youngest had been forced to move away. The cycle that began a century was again about to complete itself.

Yes, Grandmother was probably relieved to be rid of her parlor. It had turned out to be temporary; it had made its challenge and had been ignored, and what happened in it had been mostly unhappy. When Grandmother sold its furniture, she did not refurnish it as she had done some of her houses. The frowning high-backed chairs and the cabinets and table, with their thin and nervous legs, went back over the Sierras to San Francisco, and Grandmother did not use her parlor again. Instead, she locked the door.

Chapter Ten

Chapter Ten

A FEW MONTHS AGO I RECEIVED A LETTER FROM GRANDMOTHER. IT WAS much the same as the others, my address boldly written in black ink on a white watermarked envelope, but the difference was that it came by air mail.

"I hope," she said, "you were not overwhelmed with the extravagance of my postage, but I have never mailed a letter for an aeroplane before and I wanted the satisfaction of knowing something I was saying was important enough to be carried on wings.

"There is really a more urgent reason. Your mother has written that you contemplate coming to Nevada this summer. I should urge you to spend your time with more pleasure at some springs or a lake, but I would so enjoy seeing you; and if you would like to come, come as soon as you can. Forward the date but remember to come gently for Virginia City is unaccustomed to visitors and may be unable to stand the shock.

"However, I have refused many years ago to be concerned further of the city and at this time cannot resist being selfish enough to think of myself. The route to us is involved, but have patience with me and I promise to steer your course."

After a few such instructions and advice of hotels, Grandmother changed the subject to other matters, and happened to mention her clock.

"I forgot to warn you to bring your own time-piece. I have dozens of them and they are all broken. I have your grandfather's watch, but it has become increasingly eccentric and I have begun to fear for its balance. Perhaps I would do better to tell time like Willy [her wood-cutter and occasional errand boy]. Willy is distrustful of the hours but lives his day by the sun. If he has a job for the morrow, he promises to be on time 'soon in the mornin',' and he arises with a cliché, which is to say, he 'gets up with the sun.'

"I should apologize for my clock. And I would, if I knew how to spell its name. Is it 'Cucko' or is there a second o? We have persistently called it 'Coo-Coo,' but that will never do for anything as solemn as writing.

"However, I must get to my point. The clock is broken. I assure you that you won't be asked to fix it; I recall you are no handier than any city boy needs to be. I intended to ask you to bring a spring for it. And now I have changed my mind. It just occurred to me that I really don't need a clock and would be bewildered to have one. Anyway, you will not be stopping in Germany on your way here, which is where the springs are kept; and I really don't need the clock, mind you, for one should not have such a silly thing as a Coo-Coo for such a serious purpose as keeping the time.

"I am sorry to have mentioned it, and would begin this letter again except that my aeroplane is waiting."

Grandmother concluded her letter with more instructions for my trip, explaining: "Put your fate in the hands of Fred Norton. He will get you to Virginia City when hope and desperation fail."

Fred Norton had been the daring young man who drove the first automobile into the Comstock district and thus won the citizens' immediate respect. Now he drove the motor bus between Reno and Virginia City.

Following Grandmother's instructions, I found Fred Norton and his bus early one morning in Reno. His coach was wearied and yellowed, and it provided for both passengers and freight. He seemed slightly surprised to be able to sell a ticket, and he apologized casually for placing me in the back with some sacked sides of beef and a bedding roll that belonged to some one else.

Our trip had to be made over the Geiger Grade, a historically exasperating trail that climbs for twelve miles almost straight up a mountain and then levels off to a succession of bumps. The sun came down with great ambition for so early in April in Nevada. The snow melted from the banks by the side of the road, and the rocks perspired; and we bumped along with the engine wearily breathing while the sagebrush hens ran ahead of us easily, as if we were the slowest of pokes.

Our conversation was punctuated with bumps and lunges. Mr. Norton hung on to the wheel and I steadied myself on the beef while I attempted to ask questions of Virginia City. Instead, we talked about politics, which seemed to be in a worse predicament than ever. Mr. Norton conversed very carefully, to begin with, for he wanted to learn if I were a Democrat. He was himself a state senator, having been elected on the Democratic ticket. We talked of graft in public office and the class struggle, and quietly cursed the fate that held us. Finally, we agreed that something should be done about the nation's crisis, and let the problem go at that.

One becomes accustomed, after the first surprise, to learn that his bus driver or his storekeeper is a person of importance in the management of Nevada, for in the entire state there are few more people than were once in Virginia City itself, and the politicians there are not a type apart from the people.

But a senator, at any rate, can talk about politics,

and my senator—and he was an honest one—continued his explanation and argument mile after mile until at last we rounded the turn that let me see Virginia City again.

"Well," said Mr. Norton, "it hasn't changed much, has it?"

But it had changed indeed. What was left was an angry and blackened old place that from a distance looked like a bruise on the mountain side. From here it was easy to see that the city had been an accident to begin with; an accident that interrupted the length of the range and caused the high, immense, and snow-peaked mountains to close in and tower over the city to conceal it as some sort of family shame.

The city lay dry and barren, for the ridges higher up got the snow that fell from the mountain peaks. But even there moisture did not help, for the sharp wind up from Washoe swept over the mountain to leave the ground cracked and the gigantic rocks naked. There was always wind, but seldom dust with it; and even the streets of the city were bare and harsh.

Blocks of buildings were still standing; all but a few were abandoned. Two stores were left, and three saloons, thus keeping the Comstock tradition. The customary old men were sitting on the board sidewalk in front of the Crystal Saloon and near them was a saddle horse that had its reins around a hitching rail and its eye upon a small dog who was ambitiously after a flea.

The men looked upon me with surprised curiosity, but they nodded and spoke, for that is still the custom in Nevada. Their hats were low over their eyes and their eyes were squinted; they were chewing tobacco, and one of them, a very old man, had the juice of it on the white handkerchief wrapped around his neck. They had heard of Grandmother, but few of them had ever seen her; and they simply referred to her home on the hill as the Flannery Place.

The old men were mostly nomads who had drifted back to town and had been hired to work for a while in some small mine which was being reclaimed. There were younger men, too, but they had come from a company in California on a commission for mining work. Some of them lived in parts of the old houses, and some of them drove back and forth every day from Reno and Carson City. Young or old, they knew less of the town's history than the tourists who came in the summer time, for while they were the remnants of the Comstock Lode, they were not part of it, and for them Virginia City was simply another abandoned mining town.

The houses that were left were sinking into the ground. The Soda Works had sunk to its signboard and could be recognized now only because there was behind it the pile of broken glass that shone in the sunlight. The fire houses along B Street were ramshackle and loose in the wind that washed through them. The House of Tin was gone, and the big bank on C Street was closed but had a hopeful placard in its window that still maintained: SILVER DAYS WILL COME AGAIN. Next to the bank was an abandoned confectionery with a sign that said: WELCOME, GENERAL GRANT. The *Enterprise* building had the dirt of so many years on its windows that the old-fashioned high desks inside could scarcely be seen. The little hand press was a pile of dusty cobwebs and the wooden porch was precarious with cracks.

The only church left was the Catholic church. The outside of it was a rusty and weather-beaten white, but the inside was still elaborate with a silver and white altar and yellowwood beams that the years had helped. Near the altar there were many lilies that had been left from Easter Sunday. The church was large, but it was filled with the odor of the lilies.

The schoolhouse still had the responsibility of a few children, but its two upper floors were boarded up. It was recess time, and five children, of completely different sizes, were playing baseball in a courtyard of granite dust, within a hundred feet of a crew of eleven men who were digging in the street.

Grandmother had explained the men in the streets. They were digging for gold.

"You are too young to have heard of it," she wrote, "but your ancestors thought it was a capital joke that the skies once rained gold on the Comstock. I believe it was in 1871 or '81 (what does it matter?) that the Washoe Zephyr became infuriated and on a Fall afternoon railed at us until even the dogs were forced to cover. There was a lack of dust for the Zephyr to blow, but he had something better than that. When the men returned from the mines and were compelled for once to wash their faces, they discovered a glitter in the bottom of their basins. Yes, it was gold. There was great excitement.

"Of course, I would not try to convince you that gold came from the skies, as science says of the frogs; but the Comstock men were convinced, for they had washed gold from their faces.

"The gold is finally being realized. Roark Taylor has joined a crew of men who are shoveling up the streets for it. They have a truck and pile it high with dirt; they say their ore is averaging from ten to twenty dollars a ton. At any rate, they are completely destroying the streets. I suppose that the streets are the only places left that have not been mined!

"The men have been at it for months; they certainly are thorough. They move along in a row the width of the street, moving systematically and shoveling up everything. They should be at my house within three months, tearing up the street; if they hurry they can be here before the tourists, but I fear that is too much to ask."

Roark Taylor, whom Grandmother mentioned, was one of the last of the Comstock miners. Yet he had not meant to be a miner at all. He had a claim on the side of Mt. Davidson. It was part of the quartz ledge, but he had been drilling into it for years and it had not yielded much. He had not developed as steadily on it as he intended because it was necessary sometimes to work in a company mine to get enough money to buy the dynamite for his own claim. In his mine he dynamited, then shoveled clear, then dynamited. He believed he was within a week's work of a strike which would yield him enough specimen rock to sell his mine and let him come to California. After eleven years he was still within a week of it.

Roark was very old. In years he was perhaps no more than fifty, but his work had put more age than that on him. Like so many of the original hard-rock miners, he had rough features, hard and bruised, for he had been drilling into rock so long he seemed to become part of it. His ambition to be a school teacher was never fulfilled, but he managed to become a member of the school board, which let him be near schools.

He gave it up, though, for when the husband of his sister died, she needed money for herself and the children, and Roark went back to the company mines. It was too late, when the sister died and the children had grown, for Roark to get an education. Yet he had a chance to escape mining. He returned to his claim and built a shack beside it to be able to live there and work longer and harder to escape mining.

There was another reason why Roark stayed away from the city. His friends teased him. He had realized his life was incomplete; and when he was in middle age and still a bachelor he proposed marriage to a school teacher who came to Virginia City and had been kind to him. In fact, he proposed in a solemn, formal letter. The school teacher thought the method was too quaint to keep secret and showed it to other teachers in the Ward School. Roark suddenly found himself exposed as the comical bachelor who wanted to marry a young woman. He was teased by the town, for no one minded teasing old Roark who was such a good-natured and sociable man. But Roark was ashamed of himself and angry at his people; he was glad to retreat to his mine, knowing that in just a little while he could escape to California.

But all of this occurred a long time ago. Roark has since threatened to forsake the mine. He tells Grandmother that he will leave it in three or four weeks.

"I don't think it's worth a thing, Mrs. Flannery," he will say, and then add, "and I'm not a-going to give it all my life."

He will give it just three weeks more; but those weeks of course never end.

Roark often visits Grandmother, when his day's work is done, walking through the dark of Gold Hill to the Divide, which is a distance of at least seven miles. He sits in the large chair in the kitchen, talking quietly; he is always obviously delighted when Grandmother at ten o'clock spreads the table for coffee and cake, although he always insists she really mustn't bother. But Grandmother never fails to make the coffee, for to have a friend return even from town and not instantly have a cup of coffee would be unthinkable.

"I think the man's really hungry," Grandmother says. "Heaven knows what he cooks for himself in that shack! He must have nothing but meat and potatoes, and I can just see him frying and greasing everything."

Roark tried to persuade Grandmother to leave Nevada. "We both ought to be away from here, Mrs. Flannery; there's nothing for us here. We ought to go to California." Roark repeats it, as he repeats everything now.

But Roark is another story. Mine begins again when

Fred Norton had finally unloaded the beef and the bedding roll and returned from whatever serious business kept him in the post office, to start his weary bus again and drive up the hill to Grandmother.

The Ending

The Ending

GRANDMOTHER HAD NOT SEEN ME COM-
ING AND WAS SITTING ON THE SOFA
in the living room. She was wearing a light apron with
a knitted shawl drawn around her shoulders, and an
opened book was on her lap. Yet she was not reading,
for her face was in complete repose, as though she had
looked up for a moment and had been pleasantly interrupted by a recollection.

For a breath, when first she saw me, she seemed
much older, but her age faded with her surprise; and
after she had appraised and questioned, my time away
disappeared and our talk continued from where it had
been left ten years before. I might have just been to
Reno and taken longer returning than I had intended.
There were a few more questions, but not many, for
Grandmother had read the letters and she certainly
does not like to be told the same thing twice.

It was good to feel that Grandmother had not
changed. I had been apprehensive on my trip and as
soon as I saw the house, I realized I had forgotten it
was so very old. The back barns of it had dropped away

and the fence was down in many places, and even Edward's garden was gone. The seasons had done for the crab-apple tree. It stood in what had been the front garden without a leaf on it, dry and bare, and this was spring. The front gate, though, still hung on, so determined and grim indeed that I had to lift it almost from its hinges. I had left my bags by it, in the withered garden, and walked around the corner of the house to the side door, self-consciously, with my hat in my hand. Then Grandmother and the inside of the house reassured me.

The sitting room was quite the same as when I had left. There was on the wall the light oil of the reedlike Romeo and his darkish and completely plump Juliet, she with her arms clasped to her breasts and her eyes to the sky, thanking the heavens for some classical favor. In the corner where the sun never reached was the cast-iron sewing machine that Grandmother somehow never did use, and above it on the wall was the crayon portrait of Red Riding Hood which had been given to Mother when the two of them were contemporaries. Her golden curls were faded, but Red Riding Hood herself was still as blunderingly innocent as ever, intent on telling the Wolf all she knew.

The window was hung with light, cheerful curtains, and it allowed so much afternoon sunlight to enter that the sofa near by suffered and often had to be re-covered. The sofa now was light brown, the shade of a monk's gown. The corner was one of Grandmother's favorite places in the house, where she had her bookstand and her glasses and needle-work. It was very pleasant to find her there in her bright house apron and knitted shawl, on the brown sofa.

My bedroom was the same one I always had, with its deep and narrow feather bed. The door to it was held open by the little artificial stove that had been given to Grandfather by the Franklin Stove Company when he purchased the kitchen range. The room even retained the calendar I had put on the wall when I was a boy. It was in bright colors and displayed a won-derfully wholesome cowboy in the act of drawing his revolver to put an end to a coiled rattlesnake that had raised his head at the cowboy's horse. The horse's eyes were desperate, and the poor thing still had its front legs up in the air. The calendar declared that the year was 1920, and it explained that for fancy groceries N. C. Prater & Sons couldn't be beat.

The kitchen had many calendars, all of them from grocerymen. Since the grocerymen in Reno were usually Italian, their calendars were illustrations of the old-fashioned young faces, dark-haired ladies with light skin and black eyes, displaying gold earrings, such as must have been seen in the market places in

Naples, when the grocerymen sailed for the new country. Two heads were in the pictures, of mother and daughter; both with extremely innocent and trusting faces, the mother usually wearing a large and elaborate hat that bloomed about her head like a blossom. All the calendars had to be kept on the wall, or the various grocerymen would be insulted. Grandmother had to trade with all of them, a week with each one. It was quite a problem.

The kitchen was still the place for household transactions. Willy came to the kitchen door punctually at three in the afternoon, as he had done for thirty years, to chop the wood for the next day and to ask if there were errands. Willy had reached the age of fifty, but belonged to those people who are born with extraordinarily large heads that are too heavy ever to be held erect; and now when he was fifty he was told when he had done his work that he was a Good Boy. Willy considered himself a good boy except in the afternoon when he smoked a cigarette. After his work was done, Willy sat in the woodshed, smoking his cigarette and looking at it, chuckling slyly with the pleasure of his sin. Willy's sister forbade him to smoke, but Grandmother kept cigarettes for Willy and gave them to him one at a time, once a day, with a cigar on his birthday and Christmas, when his sister's family gave him socks.

Willy relies upon Grandmother and he likes to feel that she relies upon him. The friendship between them can be understood by ignoring his age and his head, but regarding him as a young man of, say, thirteen. Willy was in middle age when I was a small boy, but I had talked to him as one boy to another. He listened thoughtfully to my exaggerations and was willing to pull me in my wagon. Other boys teased him because his head rolled on his shoulders, but I could not, although I felt I was being inferior to my friends. Besides, Willy was fond of me. He carried my bundles and brought me leather quirts he had woven; and once, with great pride, he presented me with a brass watch chain and a cigar, although I had no watch and knew of no haven safe enough to smoke a cigar.

Willy had known for weeks that I was coming, and this day he dressed for the occasion in his blue serge suit that was whitened with lint, his wrinkled but clean striped shirt, and a stiff collar that was ever for Willy surprisingly white. He was being a man of the world standing there in Grandmother's woodshed, shaking hands and asking if there was any little thing he could do for me, just anything I wanted. He tried hard to talk big, but he stammered just the same, and despite his efforts he failed to keep his huge head from rolling while he was assuring me of how much Grandmother depended upon him. She stopped him gently when he had gone too far in his breathless, painful discourse.

Because the day was a great one for Willy, he was given a small glass of beer with his cigarette. He drank so hurriedly he must not have tasted it, and when he left us he was so excited he seemed to be in broken pieces. Grandmother and I watched him as he walked by the window, playing a tune with his finger on the pickets of the fence as he passed. He was as happy as a boy can be.

But Willy had not yet cut his wood. He returned in half an hour, this time in his overalls and his baggy brown coat. Although he looked directly at us, he did not speak. We were not supposed to know he was there.

"Willy's our last proud citizen," said Grandmother. "He thinks this is the best place in the world. But then, he has never been any other place, not even to Reno. I don't believe he notices that people live here no longer."

If Willy missed anyone, it must have been Grandmother's spaniel. He was very fond of the dog and when Grandmother told him the dog was as smart as a whip, Willy said that was true.

"She certainly is, Mrs. Flannery, she's as smart as a whip." And whenever after Willy described the dog, he used that phrase.

The spaniel had been a puppy when she came to the house; although many names were suggested for her, she came to be called the Spaniel. She was a water spaniel with rich black hair, a small, strong dog that lived to be twenty years old. Despite the insistence of the family, the Spaniel flatly refused to do tricks, but she did agree to one task. She helped fill the woodbox.

Grandmother would say, "Go help Willy with the wood," and the dog would run to the snowshed, her claws scratching briskly along the flooring, to carry in a stick of wood at a time and drop it into the woodbox.

The Spaniel became so old that she lost her hearing and then her consciousness, and finally one morning in winter she was dead, and Willy had to wrap her in a Piute blanket to drop her down an abandoned mine shaft. Grandmother would never have another dog.

With the Spaniel gone, Grandmother no longer took her walks in the evening or her occasional trips to town, and people have not seen her often. She even dislikes to take her trips to Reno. She would certainly not leave Nevada for California. She is not especially fond of her state, but California is a new land in another century, and the speed and clatter of it would disturb and perhaps even irritate her. Virginia City, of course, is still rough and noisy, but the Divide is a reasonably peaceful place—except for those asinine tourists and their automobiles. Indeed, she can see she is as comfortable as she could be, under the circumstances.

Yet there is no exhaustion in Grandmother. There are lines that trouble brought and aches and pain that hurt a body, but the overwhelming fatigue that causes old people to doze and confuse their dreaming with their living has not come to her.

Grandmother realizes that she is entitled to be foolish and troubled to the end. It is very pleasant for some people to request sympathy and receive it, but she has never been able to get any comfort from it. A few years ago she expected that presently the increasing number of her years would softly wear away her keen senses, and then she would be mercifully ignorant that she had become senile and bothersome. That would be merciful, but it would also be unpleasant, for old people are such a problem.

But it never happened. After she came to eighty, even her body seemed to have stopped its decline. Her hearing was good, her heart was steady, and her eyesight seemed as strong as ever. She changed the lenses once a year, but she wore glasses only while reading or sewing, and the ease with which she could thread a needle she regarded as highly indecent. Finally, when Grandmother reached eighty-five she just quit counting the years. They did not seem to matter any more.

It occurred to Grandmother that perhaps a person could be only a limited number of years old; although she knew it was absurd to say it. One always grew older: there was no getting around that. Yet, she had accepted age without resistance, and now she was not so old as she should be. She had been as old as her friends, but they were gone. They had been pathetic. They talked of death, always of death, or a friend who had just died or was dying, or of some one who was waiting to die. Death preoccupied them. They had tried to embrace or to flee from it, when they should have been patient.

The ninety years rest gracefully on Grandmother. She seems to be completely satisfied to remain every day in her home. The days go no more quickly, but they have formed their pattern to follow. Grandmother dislikes the hours and refuses to obey them. All of her clocks have stopped, and she never remembers at a convenient time to have them repaired. The cuckoo clock stands silent in the hall, and Grandmother declares that its interrupted expression and staring face is a reproach. Yet she disregards it, for she believes it is better for a day to be in three periods. The morning occurs in the kitchen, and when the sun is shining the afternoon comes casually to the side porch, and afterward it is evening in the sitting room.

There are books to be read; not new books, but books she has read many times before, of Emerson and Washington Irving and Gibbon and that youthful rascal Mr. Shaw. There is no need now even to read the newspaper. While Grandmother is aware of the changes that time and a day bring, she is no longer curious, for the quiet anticipation of her life has flowed into serenity and she has come to a place where she pauses patiently, while the rest of us go on without her.

I remember that Grandmother maintained her schedule every day I was there except on the morning that I was to leave. I was to leave early, but she was up before me, and the heat from the kitchen was coming back to the rest of the house. Grandmother was wearing her gray linen house dress, and her apron was a very gay red. She must have been up hours, for even her hair was combed already. Passing her room, I noticed that the basin was on her bureau and her silver comb was beside it. They formed a pattern against the stiff white of the starched covering.

It was going to be a bad day for my trip, Grandmother said, for the wind was up already. There might be a storm. But we could watch for it while we had breakfast. Grandmother had made the coffee on the range and had taken the toast from the oven. She had an electric toaster, a Christmas gift, but she never used it. She did use another Christmas gift, though: an egg-timer. I had given it to her at least fifteen years ago, while I was living with her. It hangs even now over the kitchen table, and she refers to it every morning, watching the sand slip down into the glass, for Grandmother is very particular about her eggs.

I told Grandmother it was an especial honor to have her at the breakfast table, but she said that was nonsense.

"I wouldn't have you puttering around the kitchen," she said. "I would trust you anywhere but there."

After breakfast we stood at the window with my bags at the kitchen door. Grandmother was anticipating the storm. The thickness was gathering, and the men who had been digging for gold in the streets were gone to cover; Virginia City down below looked like a reflection on wavering water. The great black holes cut into the earth were drawing together, and the houses in the city were settling down, as though they were elderly persons on their way back to the earth. There was dust in the air. The wind must have carried it for miles from the other side of the mountain.

Through the thickness we could see Mr. Norton's bus come grumbling up the hill to the Divide. Grandmother got her shawl from the chair by the stove, and we left the house to wait in the yard. With the dust there was a rawness in the air that suggested snow and stung our cheeks. In a moment the bus came to the gate, to stop with a shudder. Mr. Norton waved his hand and jumped down. He took off his cap and bowed to Grandmother.

"Don't come any further, Mrs. Flannery," he said. "You'll catch your death a-cold in this weather."

Then he hurried my bags into the back of the bus. Mr. Norton looked back to see if I was ready. He speeded the motor and my grandmother smiled as the engine protested. We left there in a hurry as the wind was blowing, and Grandmother returned into her house, where the clocks no longer tell the time.